HOSPITAL HILL

AN ILLUSTRATED ACCOUNT
OF PUBLIC HEALTHCARE INSTITUTIONS
IN KANSAS CITY, MISSOURI

JAMES L. SOWARD

The information on page 71 is taken from *Good Morning Blues: The Autobiography of Count Basie* by Count Basie, as told to Albert Murray. Copyright © 1985 by Albert Murray and Count Basie Enterprises, Inc. Reprinted by permission of Random House, Inc.

II

First printing 1995

Printed in the United States of America

ISBN 0-932845-71-1

CONTENTS

FOREWORD

September 23, 1995

This book is a testimonial to 125 years of public healthcare and training on Hospital Hill. The people on this campus have cared for the sick and needy and trained healthcare professionals to treat the ills of Kansas Citians longer than anyone in our community. Hospital Hill's staying power is evidenced by its survival through times of adversity as well as its growth in times of need. On this 125th anniversary, Hospital Hill is experiencing perhaps its most significant physical growth spurt . . . again in response to the needs of those served by the health and teaching institutions which make up the campus.

The chronicling of this fascinating history took foresight, dedication, cooperation, and money. The Truman Medical Center Charitable Foundation envisioned and coordinated this project thanks to the leadership of Don Smithburg. The School of Medicine at the University of Missouri-Kansas City donated the services of the author, Jim Soward, to bring the past back to life. The Children's Mercy Hospital, The Eye Foundation of Kansas City, Hospital Hill Health Services Corporation, Kansas City Health Department, Truman Medical Center and its Charitable Foundation, the School of Medicine Alumni Association and Western Missouri Mental Health Center all contributed human and financial resources to publish this book. The University of Missouri-Kansas City central administration provided key advice to the project.

Special thanks go to the many Hospital Hill staff and board veterans, as well as civic leaders, whose service exemplifies the campus's achievements and whose memory contributed greatly to the development of this historical account of Kansas City's original health system.

IV

E. J. Holland, Jr.
President, Board of Directors
Truman Medical Center Charitable Foundation

In 1840, French trappers and fur traders built cabins and storehouses near the Missouri River, along what is now the East Bottoms, below the mouth of the Kaw (Kansas) River. Three decades later, the sandbar island on the right served the City of Kansas as the site of a pest house.

INTRODUCTION

SEAS, GLACIERS, FORESTS . . . AND PORTER PROPERTY

Nineteen ninety-five marks the 125th anniversary of the establishment of Kansas City, Missouri's first public hospital. In 1870, the City of Kansas established a small frame structure to treat indigent patients on property it had purchased in 1867 from Elijah M. "Milt" McGee. Although the hospital location lay outside the city, not an unusual practice during that period, it sat just two blocks from the 20th Street southern boundary. This site, in one form or another, has accommodated institutions that have served the healthcare needs of citizens of Kansas City, Jackson County and the State of Missouri for a century and a quarter.

This book attempts to depict in words and pictures
- the development of these healthcare institutions
- the public health crises that arose from floods, epidemics and disasters, both natural and human-made
- the influence of early-day city and county politics in public healthcare matters
- the aging of public health physical facilities that many institutions experienced, some fatally
- the era of desegregation and the introduction of Medicare and Medicaid that brought with them new care delivery challenges.

Most of all, it seeks to describe the collaboration of city, county, state and federal governments with civic foundations, private citizens, charitable organizations, healthcare officials and educators that conceived and contributed to the growth of the truly unique metropolitan healthcare complex in Kansas City we know as Hospital Hill.

Hospital Hill also attempts to tell briefly the story of some other Kansas City institutions that have given care to indigent citizens. Institutions come

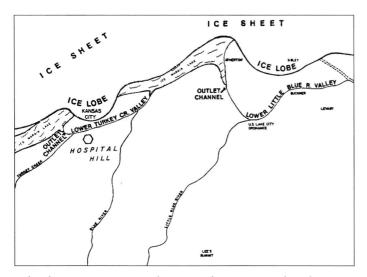

The drainage system at the time of maximum glacial advance about 600,000 years ago. Meltwater diverted around an ice lobe that dammed the Kansas River and eroded Lower Turkey Creek Valley. After the ice lobe collapsed the Kansas River resumed its prior course and the Lower Turkey Creek Valley filled with alluvial deposits of sand and gravel. Union Station rests on this alluvial-filled valley, the principal rail access route into Kansas City south of the Missouri River.

The Rev. James Porter built this cabin at the present northeast corner of 28th and Tracy with the help of slaves he brought from Tennessee. View: NW to SE.

and go, so the histories of some worthy caregivers may not appear here. In many cases the ready availability of photographs and reliable printed material guided our selections. For those we omit, we apologize. Our original intent in publishing this book was to recount brief histories in word and illustration of the several institutions and organizations that comprise the present-day Hospital Hill complex. It soon became apparent that the histories of other Kansas City healthcare institutions intertwined with ours. And so we have included accounts of facilities that also served the poor or disadvantaged of Kansas City and Jackson County.

We also relate in this book the stories of several individuals who worked, trained, served and often fought for the many institutions that cared for the indigent ill of the region for the past 125 years. It is often through the actions and principles of such individuals that institutions thrive or wither and die. Our institution of Hospital Hill survives, thanks to many who came before us.

Readers may find it hard to imagine that ancient seas covered the land we call Hospital Hill several times, sometimes to a depth of hundreds of feet, or that glacial meltwater and ice lobes spilled through our area to carve out huge valleys. The story of those seas and glaciers appears everywhere around us on the Hill in street cuts and excavations, and explains in part why those early pioneers who erected hospitals built them on high ground. Richard Gentile, professor of Geosciences at the University of Missouri-Kansas City, offers an excellent monograph of the local geology in Appendix B at the end of this book.

Several ironies abound in the parallel histories of Hospital Hill and Kansas City. One colleague has suggested that this offering should have been two books. For sidetracks or forks in the road herein, I accept responsibility and do not expect you will miss much if you pass them by. It seems ironic, though, that the bulk of the land which our buildings occupy once belonged to a Methodist minister, the Reverend James Porter, who used slaves to build his cabin in a dense, forested landscape some 161 years ago. On that same site today stands a school dedicated to the care of handicapped children, many of them black. Of further note, the same hospital system had to wheel deceased patients across hospital grounds to almost inaccessible morgues because of faulty building plans, once in 1930 at General Hospital #2 and again at the Diagnostic and Treatment Center in 1962. It seems ironic, too, that during the 1920s and 1930s people stood in line at 1908 Main to ask Boss Tom Pendergast for political favors and money while at the same time people stood in line at 200 Main to ask another man, William Volker, for philanthropic favors and money. Indeed, the Truman Medical Center Charitable Foundation itself formed in 1979 from a $625,000 gift from the Volker Trust.

One final irony. In 1855, Robert Van Horn, the city's first successful newspaper owner and a future U.S. congressman, and Milt McGee, the man who sold the land to the city for the first public hospital and a member of the Kansas territorial legislature, attempted unsuccessfully to fix the western boundary of Missouri on its present line until it came north to the point where the line crossed the Blue River just south of Martin City. The Missouri state line would then follow the Big Blue until it emptied at its mouth in the Missouri River, miles east of here. That certainly would have solved forever the confusion about Kansas City, Missouri in the minds of people who think it belongs in Kansas. It might also have solved a few of our past and present-day state-line differences.

If you ponder the future of public healthcare in the next millennium, take solace that many others do so as well. But if you wonder how we arrived at this present-day situation, read on.

James L. Soward

Porter died in 1851. The Porter family later disinterred his body and reburied him in the family plot in Union Cemetery on the same north-facing bluff as Hospital Hill. View: SW to NE.

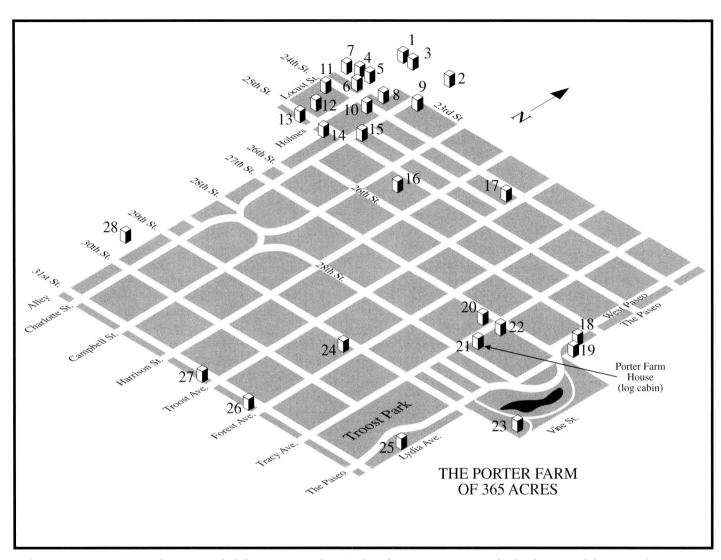

The Rev. James Porter's farm extended from present-day 23rd and Locust to 31st and Charlotte, and from 23rd to 31st and The Paseo.

MAP KEY

1	Western Missouri Mental Health Center.	16	Longfellow Heights Apartments.
2	Central Kansas City Mental Health Services (Felix Building).	17	Future Health Department building.
3	UMKC School of Nursing.	18	Former Christian Church Hospital, VA Hospital and Robinson Neurological Clinic.
4	Health Department (Todd Hall).	19	Former Christian Church Hospital Nurses' Residence, Fairmount Maternity Hospital and presently Welcome House, Inc.
5	Eye Foundation of Kansas City.		
6	Hospital Hill Center.		
7	Children's Mercy Hospital outpatient and parking facility.	20	Former Krestwoods Hospital.
8	Truman Medical Center.	21	Former Porter family cabin and presently B. W. Sheperd State School for the Severely Handicapped.
9	Truman Medical Center parking facility.		
10	UMKC School of Medicine.	22	Former Hall family mansion.
11	Children's Mercy Hospital.	23	Former Lakeside Hospital.
12	UMKC School of Dentistry.	24	Former Punton Sanitarium (first).
13	Ronald McDonald House.	25	Former Punton Sanitarium (second).
14	Diastole and the Kiva.	26	Former Walt Disney studio.
15	Konomos, Inc. (Formerly Kansas City Film Ad Company.)	27	Former Wirthman Building and Isis Theater.
		28	Longfellow School.

GUIDE TO INITIALISMS AND ABBREVIATIONS

We use the following initialisms in this book to avoid the repetition of printing long names:

INSTITUTIONS OR AGENCIES

CMH	Children's Mercy Hospital (The)
EFKC	Eye Foundation of Kansas City
HHHSC	Hospital Hill Health Services Corporation
GH	General Hospital (or GH #1, GH #2, etc.)
GKCMHF	Greater Kansas City Mental Health Foundation
JCMS	Jackson County Medical Society
KCGH	Kansas City General Hospital
KCGH&MC	Kansas City General Hospital & Medical Center
TMC	Truman Medical Center (West or East)
TMCCF	Truman Medical Center Charitable Foundation
UMC	University Medical College
UMKC	University of Missouri-Kansas City SOM-School of Medicine SOD-School of Dentistry SOP-School of Pharmacy SON-School of Nursing
WMMHC	Western Missouri Mental Health Center

After an 1826 flood washed away Francois Chouteau's original settlement, he moved his post to higher ground, shown here in 1830, near where Troost Avenue now intersects the Missouri River.

In this 1852 drawing of the Town of Kansas, what appears to be a sandbar island lies downstream from a steamboat.

2

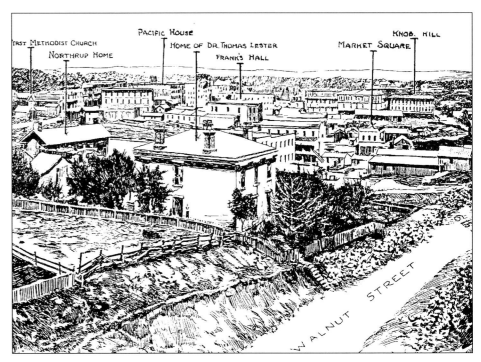

In 1868, Kansas City's version of Nob Hill overlooked the river. View: SE to NW from 6th and Walnut.

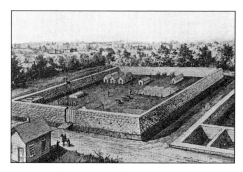

The Union Army converted McGee's Hotel, on the east side of Grand between 16th and 17th, to a hospital during the Civil War.

During the war, Federal troops used the foundation of the unfinished Coates House Hotel for cavalry stables.

CHAPTER ONE

TOWNSHIP 50, RANGE 33 WEST

The rivers brought the people to the city on the bluff. The land, made rich by the rivers, kept the people there. And even the early historians knew the importance geography played in making Kansas City a place of good times and bad.

In 1858, C.C. Spalding, the town's principal civic booster, wrote that Kansas City "has always been a prominent point for the business of the plains." Sitting at the confluence of two great rivers and on the edge of a vast treeless prairie opening to the promise of the West, the town offered much to traders, immigrants, stockmen, entrepreneurs and land speculators. It served as a river landing and storehouse for goods going to the town of Westport and on across the plains, as a convenient stopping place for wagon trains headed from Independence to Santa Fe, or to California or Oregon, as a rail center for travelers headed west and as a supplier of grain, beef and pork for the burgeoning populations of the East.

Despite Spalding's glowing accounts, the Town of Kansas offered a hostile environment for most who lived and worked here. Once past the river levees, the lack of usual community amenities became evident. In 1872, John C. McCoy, a pioneer settler, recalled Kansas City in earlier days as a "clearing, or old field, of a few acres, lying on the high ridge between Main and Wyandotte and Second and Fifth streets . . . On all sides a dense forest, the ground covered with impenetrable underbrush and fallen timber, and deep impassable gorges."

As always, waterways defined the city: the Missouri River on the north; the Kaw River, or the Kansas, to the west; on the east the Big Blue and Little Blue Rivers with their many tributaries; and to the south and west, three creeks: O.K., Brush and Turkey.

Spring rains often created stagnant pools and sloughs along the creek valleys and river bottoms. In June 1844, a great flood occurred. McCoy later wrote that the volume of water that swept down the Kaw "madly rushing against the mighty Missouri caused the seething waters to pile up at the mouth, no doubt

3

Main Street, 1868. Several brick buildings and a drugstore gave an air of permanence to early Kansas City. View: S to N from Missouri Avenue.

4

The first medical publication in the city lasted little more than a year. When the Civil War erupted, the two editors and publishers – former mayor G.M.B. Maughs and Theodore S. Case – joined opposite sides. Maughs joined the Confederate forces; Case enlisted in the Union Army.

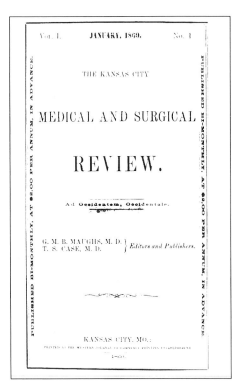

several feet higher than they would have done had they met at the point of junction more obliquely."

The Kansas City Times reported in its edition of July 27, 1872: "The doctors are resting, confidently expectant of the brisk and busy times when the hot sun shall begin to boil the stagnant water ponds and raise the poisonous malaria."

Dr. Leo Twyman, the first medical authority to write of the abundance of water in the local area and its effect on the health of the people, arrived in Independence in 1844. He practiced medicine there for a quarter of a century, and his journal notes and later those of his son, Dr. Lyddall Twyman, describe vividly the health hazards of early Jackson County.

Leo Twyman wrote: "It is quite important for settlers and immigrants what sections of the county are most healthful. . . . Adjacent to all these streams are bottom lands, more or less extensive, nearly along their whole course on one side, and bluffs or hills on the other. . . . In the larger bottoms are a number of small ponds or lakes, and spots of marshy ground which are filled with water the greater part of the year, and in rainy seasons become quite extensive, which evaporate and dry up in the hot, dry seasons usually following, in the months of July, August and September, and thus generate the poisonous exhalation about which so little is known, and called by physicians 'miasm' or 'malaria.' " More of the Twymans' observations appear in the local timeline later in this chapter.

In many ways, the problems faced by the Town of Kansas mirrored the national experience. The development of the river port as the jumping-off point to the new and vibrant West brought with it the misery of poor sanitation from hordes of travelers as they arrived by wagon, steamboat and horseback. The many creeks, the marshy bottom lands and the crowds became sources of contagious diseases as the population spiraled upward. Asiatic cholera, smallpox, typhoid fever, typhus, diphtheria, dysentery, catarrh, erysipelas, rheumatic fever and whooping cough were just a few of the diseases common during Kansas City's early growth.

Many who treated the victims called themselves doctors, but few held medical degrees of any sort. Often these healers treated the sick with herbs, patent medicines or quackery. But Kansas City wasn't alone in its lack of medical prowess. Of the more than 60,000

In 1852, Jackson County bought 160 acres from Col. Henry W. Younger to build a poor farm. This early drawing depicts four structures the county built to house aged, mentally ill, alcoholic and drug-addicted indigent patients.

Immigrants' wagons at 2nd and Delaware, 1869. Pioneers who traveled west often became victims of or acted as carriers for epidemic diseases.

physicians in the U.S. in 1860, barely 20,000 held medical degrees.

Although the Town of Kansas found itself in an ideal place to take advantage of the great westward push of the 1800s, the topography of the new village created challenges for its inhabitants. The tree-covered hills and ravines behind the river bluffs posed other difficulties. From a steamboat landing at the foot of Broadway, a single road wide enough only for one wagon accommodated all freighters that carried their goods to Westport. The road led through a deep ravine, across McGee (O.K.) Creek and up the hill over the highest point of land for miles. In 1857 alone, 125 steamboats unloaded 75 million pounds of merchandise, a brisk enough trade that the town began to grade roads from the levee to Fifth Street, Broadway to Grand.

By 1861, the town had prospered enough to attract the attention of the railroads. The Pacific of Missouri Railroad from St. Louis and the Hannibal & St. Joseph Railroad from Cameron had almost completed their routes to Kansas City from the east. The rival cities of Leavenworth, Atchison and St. Joseph vied with the City of Kansas for a bridge across the Missouri River — a bridge that would almost certainly bring increased trade and population to the already overcrowded river port. With the outbreak of the Civil War the railroads temporarily suspended plans for the bridge.

The war brought additional hardship for Kansas City and its people. For the next four years, while most doctors joined one army or the other, citizens of Kansas City, also with divided loyalties, depended on two physicians for medical care, Dr. Thomas B. Lester and Dr. Isaac M. Ridge. Southern and northern sympathizers alike called on them, particularly on Ridge, who maintained a medical neutrality. Even so, the bitterness of the war meant that neither side would trust Ridge entirely. On several occasions, he tended wounded men only after their companions led Ridge blindfolded to his patients.

In October 1864, Union and Confederate armies clashed in the Battle of Westport. Ridge and Lester, along with physicians from nearby communities, cared for northern and southern wounded alike in such makeshift hospitals as the Methodist Church at Fifth Street near Wyandotte, and Lockridge Hall downtown.

With the end of the war, work began again toward a bridge across the Missouri River. In 1869, the Hannibal Bridge opened at Kansas City. Progress and prosperity lay ahead, yet the city still lacked a hospital, even a private one. Two physicians, A. B. Taylor and E. W. Schauffler, came forward that year to urge working-class men to vote for a bond to build a city hospital. It would be a hospital, Taylor and Schauffler vowed, where those working men and their wives and children could get decent medical care.

EDWARD WILLIAM SCHAUFFLER, M.D.

Edward William Schauffler was born September 11, 1839, in Vienna, Austria, the son of a missionary to Turkey. He came to the U.S. to complete his education at Williams College, served in the Union Army as a first lieutenant, then studied medicine at the College of Surgeons in New York, where he received his medical degree in 1868. In 1932, a Jackson County Medical Society biography of Schauffler stated: "(H)e had more to do with the establishing of our hospital than any other physician ... (H)e succeeded in getting the City Council to pass a bond proposal ... rolled up his sleeves and personally canvassed every working man in Kansas City ... (T)he bonds passed."

Schauffler's autobiographical account in a 1900 publication recalled the event.

"*When I came to Kansas City (1868) there wasn't a hospital in the place, not even a private hospital. The younger doctors saw the necessity of such an institution, but the older ones — the mossbacks — fought the idea vigorously. The young doctors started a boom for a city hospital. I was one of them. Three or four of us got together in 1869 and had some lawyers draw up a bill to vote funds for a city hospital. I forget how much we wanted. A special election was called to decide the matter whether the bonds should be voted. Then we young doctors went hard to work to persuade men to vote the bonds. The older doctors and the other mossbacks fought us hard and steadily. At 5 o'clock the vote seemed overwhelmingly against us. Made desperate by this, we young doctors started out to bring in voters. We rode about town arguing, pleading and begging with men to vote for the hospital. We would ride up to a group of working men at work on a building and call out to them: 'Do you want a free city hospital in this town — a hospital that won't cost you a cent? Then go to the polls right away and vote for it.' We persuaded the bosses to let the men off the job to vote for us. The result of our hard work was that the mossbacks were beaten and the town got its first hospital.*

"*The principal credit for this work is due to Dr. A.B. Taylor, who has long been dead. In Dr. Taylor's mind the idea was first born to have a city hospital in Kansas City. He lived long enough to see his idea carried out.*"

Edward William Schauffler, pictured here five decades after he led a crusade for a hospital for the working class of the city. In 1911, he directed the tuberculosis pavilion that William Volker helped establish on city hospital grounds.

1821	Missouri enters the union as a slave state.		uses nitrous oxide as an anesthetic during surgery.	1849	First American woman physician, Elizabeth Blackwell, M.D.
1828	Andrew Jackson wins U.S. presidency.	1845	University of Missouri opens a medical college in St. Louis.	1850	Missouri State Medical Association organizes.
1836	Indian tribes relocate from Missouri to western territories.	1846	First public use of ether as an anesthetic.	1859	American Dental Association forms.
1840	Baltimore College of Dental Surgery opens. First dental college in the world.	1846	Semmelweiss introduces hand washing hygiene.	1860	Florence Nightingale founds the first nursing school in London.
1844	Connecticut dentist Horace Wells	1847	Formation of the American Medical Association.	1860	New York Medical College opens the first children's clinic.

1821·1869

1821 Francois Chouteau establishes a fur trading post on the Missouri River.

1826 December 15. Jackson County organizes.

1828 Henry W. Younger, father of the infamous Younger boys, operates a ferry across the Missouri River near Randolph Bluffs.

1830 Mormons establish Colesville, near present-day Troost Lake at 27th and Paseo.

1833 John C. McCoy prepares a plat for the town of Westport.

1833 Local citizens drive Mormon settlers from the area.

1834 Methodist minister James Porter purchases land on which much of Hospital Hill stands today.

1838 "Westport Landing" becomes river destination for goods to Westport.

1844 Twyman: "June ... great flood ... July ... very dry and hot ... sickness general throughout the state."

Dr. Leo Twyman and his son, Dr. Lyddall Twyman, chronicled the health of Jackson Countians from 1844 to 1880. Three later generations of Twymans practiced medicine in the county.

1845 Twyman: "May ... heaviest rains ever ... August ... sickness commenced ... more malignant type ... still quite manageable."

1846 Twyman: "(S)ummer ... epidemic of scarlet fever ... fall ... jaundice."

1847 Dr. Benoist Troost, first physician in Kansas City.

1848 Isaac Ridge, M.D., begins a medical practice in Kansas City.

1848 Dr. F. A. Rice, a physician, opens the first drug store.

1849 Twyman: "April ... smallpox among immigrants ... May 6 ... Asiatic cholera ... great malignancy ... hotels crowded ... seven deaths in the first twenty-four hours ... fevers in August, September and October."

1850 "Westport Landing" incorporates as the Town of Kansas: 256 acres, population 500.

1850 Jackson County census lists 51 physicians, eight druggists, and one dentist.

1851 Twyman: "(C)holera again made its appearance ... excessively malignant ... May to August ... followed by fever."

1852 Jackson County purchases 160 acres in the center of the county from Col. Henry W. Younger.

1852 Twyman: "(F)all ... and winter ... pneumonia of a typhoid character ... epidemic erysipelas ... also ... a typhoid character."

John C. McCoy, an early settler, helped found both Westport and the Town of Kansas. Kansas City later named a street for him that ran between Holmes and Cherry, 21st to 25th.

1853 The Town of Kansas changes its name to the City of Kansas.

1854 Twyman: "June ... drouth ... cholera again ... more than any previous year ... considerable fever in August and September."

1855 Twyman: "(L)ate in the fall ... typhoid fever ... scarlet fever."

1855 G. W. Tindall, pioneer dentist, begins practice in the city.

1855 R. T. Van Horn becomes editor of the first successful K.C. newspaper.

Dr. A. B. Taylor served as a Union Army surgeon in the Civil War. In 1869, he founded the College of Physicians and Surgeons with Dr. Simeon Seymour Todd. Taylor played a role in getting voter approval of a bond issue in 1869 for a municipal hospital.

8

1861	Kansas becomes the 34th state.
1861	April. Civil war begins in the U.S.
1862	French chemist Louis Pasteur experiments with a "germ theory" to develop a process to destroy disease-causing organisms.
1864	Dentist William Bonwill develops a superior dental articulator.
1865	English physician Joseph Lister first uses an antiseptic agent in surgery.
1866	Mary Baker Eddy founds the principles of Christian Science.
1866	Lucy Beaman Hobbs becomes first woman in the world to receive a dental degree.
1867	Lister confirms that antiseptics and cleanliness prevent infection in wounds.
1867	Harvard establishes the first university-affiliated dental college.
1868	Howard University School of Medicine opens in Washington, D.C.
1868	Invention of the first electric dentistry drill.
1869	Robert Tanner Freeman becomes the first African-American to receive a university dental degree.

1856	Dr. T. B. Lester begins his medicine practice in the city.
1857	City founders establish Union Cemetery.
1858	Twyman: "Early in August fevers commenced ... more sickness than in any year since 1845."
1859	The city charter charges the city council with establishing hospitals and regulating them.
1860	K.C. population: 4,418. Jackson County population: 22,913.
1861	Federal troops establish Fort Union in Kansas City.

Joshua Thorne, a homeopathic physician, supervised the Union Army hospital in Kansas City during the Civil War. Thorne later helped found the Kansas City College of Medicine.

1864	Twyman: "(D)ysentery ... followed by typhoid fever."
1864	Union and Confederate forces fight in the Battle of Westport.
1865	Twyman: "Dysentery again ... fever (very violent) ... smallpox ... typhoid fever."
1866	City appoints Dr. A. P. Lankford as the first city physician.
1866	St. Joseph's Academy opens at the SW corner of 11th and Washington.
1866	A cholera epidemic breaks out, killing 117. Immigrants from St. Louis land at the river levee with the disease. David R. Porter, a local physician, writes: "Some ten or twelve who landed from the (steamboat) 'War Eagle' were taken out by Union Cemetery, and placed in a tent . . . (N)early all died."
1867	First gas lights in Kansas City.
1867	The city purchases land for hospital use for $1,800.
1867	Dr. S. S. Todd becomes city physician.
1867	The John Campbell Company, a volunteer fire brigade, forms.
1867	St. Joseph's Academy changes its name to St. Teresa's Academy.
1868	D'Estaing Dickerson, M.D., serves as city physician.

After the Civil War, Col. Theodore S. Case helped found and served as first president of the Provident Association, a forerunner of Community Chest and United Way. He also wrote a comprehensive history of Kansas City.

1868	Twyman: "(S)ome typhoid fever ... not of a very malignant type."
1869	Trains from St. Louis cross the new Hannibal Bridge.
1869	Two proprietary medical colleges open.
1869	The Kansas City Medical Society forms.
1869	A grasshopper swarm blights the region.
1869	City passes a bond issue to establish a municipal hospital.

Topographical map of Kansas City, 1869.

COMPENDIUM OF CAUSES AND EPIDEMIC DISEASES

CAUSES

bacteria: minute unicellular organisms that reside in the bodies of all living organisms. Harmless and beneficial bacteria far outnumber harmful varieties, but pathogenic forms of bacterial parasites cause disease.

virus: submicroscopic infectious agent. Viruses exist only in living tissue and do not possess a cellular structure like that of other living organisms. Viruses can cause measles, mumps, smallpox, yellow fever, polio, flu, diarrhea, meningitis, AIDS, the common cold and many other diseases.

disease carrier: animal, person or entity that acts as an intermediary in carrying an infective organism to a healthy being. Insects commonly act as carriers.

DISEASES

AIDS (acquired immune deficiency syndrome): a viral disease that suppresses the human immune system and renders it susceptible to various infections and malignancies. Spreads through certain body fluids and secretions.

cholera (Asiatic cholera): acute infectious inflammation of the intestine prevalent in warm regions where filth and poor sanitary facilities occur commonly.

diphtheria: acute contagious disease that usually occurs in children. Symptoms include sore throat and fever.

dysentery: inflammation of the intestine; widespread in unsanitary, densely populated regions through pollution of food or drink. Carriers: bacteria, viruses, chemicals, worms.

influenza (grippe): acute viral infection of the respiratory tract. Symptoms include fever, chills, headache, sore throat, cough, muscle pain and gastrointestinal problems.

poliomyelitis (polio): acute contagious viral disease that attacks the central nervous system, injures or destroys the nerve cells that control the muscles and often causes paralysis.

scarlet fever (scarlatina): acute communicable streptococcal infection that commonly occurs in young children from droplet spray, and contaminated articles, food, and milk.

smallpox (variola): highly contagious, often fatal viral disease that produces blisters and pustules on the skin.

tuberculosis (consumption, "White Plague," TB): contagious bacterial disease, commonly pulmonary, spread through inhalation of air or dust, through ingestion from contaminated food or utensils. Nonwhite races are especially vulnerable.

typhoid fever: acute bacterial infection acquired from contaminated water, milk and food, frequently in urban communities from food-handler carriers.

typhus: infectious bacterial disease carried from person to person by infected body lice. Symptoms: chills, fever, prostration, and rash.

yellow fever: acute infectious viral disease transmitted by the bite of the female mosquito, which breeds in stagnant water near human habitations. Symptoms: fever, chills, and congestion of the eyes, gums, and tongue.

Vaughan's Diamond, or the Junction Building, served as the home of the city's first medical school in 1869. View: S to N.

City Hospital burned in 1874. Although the fire destroyed the building and its records, city physician D'Estaing Dickerson managed to retain health department statistics concerning patient procedures.

12

In 1878, St. Joseph's built this central structure next to the 1874 renovated residence at 702 Pennsylvania (demolished) that served as the original hospital building. St. Joseph's added the three-story wing on the left in 1888 and the five-story building on the right in 1900. View: SE to NW.

CHAPTER TWO

THE TOWN THAT GREW TOO FAST

At 7th and Washington, Kansas City Medical College enjoyed access to a teaching environment at St. Joseph's Hospital, a block away at 7th and Pennsylvania. View: SE to NW.

In 1886, the German Hospital Association acquired the former residence of Mr. and Mrs. James Boyd Henri for $10,000 to convert into a hospital. Hospital Hill Center now stands on the site.

For decades, historians have debated the date when Kansas City built its first municipal hospital. Almost all sources, from 1888 on, have set the year as 1870, but no documentation exists to prove it. A fire in 1874 that destroyed the City Hospital also destroyed records that might have established the exact year of its founding.

On October 10, 1867, the city passed Ordinance No. 5526 "appropriating money for hospital purposes." Most authorities agree the $1,800 the city ordinance called for represented the price Milt McGee received for the land at 22nd Street and McCoy. Ordinance No. 6309 in 1868 called for "an addition to the present hospital building, privy and cistern, and authorizing the purchase of a cookstove and six beds a building." The ordinance further designated that the addition should be 50 (?) feet long, 18 feet wide and one story high. One historian, Edward A. Christ, has noted that the physician Edward W. Schauffler observed that in 1869 "no hospital existed, not even a private one." Christ also wrote: "Prior to that time, the care of the sick was managed on a catch-as-catch-can basis as early as about 1840, with private dwelling places, barns, and various outbuildings commandeered when the occasion arose in which to house custodially chiefly the epidemic sick when their number or private means left no other recourse."

The cholera epidemic in 1866 had convinced the city of the need to establish a quarantine building, which might account for the use of the word "hospital" for the more indelicate "pest house" in the ordinance. Ordinance No. 2243, dated March 6, 1871, called for "improvement of the hospital grounds and the erection of an additional building, a cistern and a fence." In 1872, the city passed Ordinance No. 5126 "to issue bonds for the erection of a hospital . . . for $12,000" and a 20-year mortgage, subject to a general election in April. Again, in August 1873, Ordinance No. 10152 directed "that a building shall be erected on the hospital grounds, and south of the present hospital buildings." No copies of contemporary city news-

13

A sandbar island in the Missouri River, opposite the East Bottoms, near a distillery, where Mayor R.H. Hunt placed an isolation house during the small-pox outbreak in 1872.

14

Edward W. Schauffler published and edited this medical journal from 1871 until 1875.

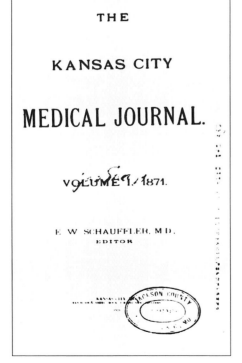

THE

KANSAS CITY

MEDICAL JOURNAL.

VOLUME 1. 1871.

E. W. SCHAUFFLER, M.D.
EDITOR

papers remain to clarify the date or to pinpoint which City Hospital building burned in 1874.

Even though the city charter of 1853 authorized the city council to enact measures to prevent and confine contagious diseases, no specific health authority existed until 1866 when the fear of cholera prompted the council to appoint a city physician, Dr. A. P. Lankford, who also served as health officer. The health officer conducted inspections, made reports, kept vital statistics and oversaw all city health matters. In 1867, the city amended the 1863 charter to give the council power to enact regulations for public health and to appoint a board of health composed of five physicians. The council appointed a new city physician, Dr. S. S. Todd, and organized a sanitary system. In 1868, Dr. D'Estaing Dickerson became city physician under that board. This board, although ineffective, existed until 1878 when the council created a new board of health that consisted of six members appointed by the mayor to represent the six city wards.

In 1869, voters approved a city bond issue for a hospital, and two proprietary medical colleges opened, the Kansas City College of Physicians and Surgeons under the guidance of Dr. Todd, the second city physician; and the Kansas City Medical College under the leadership of Dr. Lankford, the first city physician. Todd's school opened on the fourth floor of a building at the southwest corner of Eighth and Main streets, and Lankford's school rented quarters at Vaughan's Diamond, also known as the Junction Building, at Delaware, Main and Ninth streets. In 1870, the two competing colleges merged as The College of Physicians and Surgeons and remained in the Junction Building. A third medical college had also formed in 1869, the Kansas City Hospital Medical College. Several physicians excluded from the faculty of the other colleges, among them Drs. Franklin Cooley, Joseph Chew, J.O. Day and A.L. Chapman, organized and operated the school until it disbanded in 1873.

In 1866, the Sisters of St. Joseph of Carondelet had opened St. Joseph's Academy, a school for young women, on Quality Hill. It changed its name the next year to St. Teresa's Academy. The Sisters also had established a small clinic in the neighborhood to care for indigents. On October 10, 1874, the Sisters opened the first private hospital in the city in what had been the

Despite the name on the side, the first mule- and horse-drawn streetcars in Kansas City didn't go all the way to Westport. The 1870 car line ran from 4th and Main E to Walnut, S to 11th, E to Grand and S to the barn at 16th Street. In 1871, Nehemiah Holmes extended the line to Westport.

Nehemiah Holmes signed this ticket sometime before 1873. The opposite side of the ticket states: "Passengers are not allowed to sell these tickets on the cars."

In 1887, O.K. Creek, for many years an open sewer, ran from outside the eastern city limits west through Kansas City and emptied into Turkey Creek, which flowed into the Kaw (Kansas) River. O.K. Creek paralleled the east-west railroad tracks that now run through Union Station.

In 1871, the bluffs above the Missouri River bottoms posed problems both sanitary and perilous. This stereoscopic image bears the inscription: "Bluffs – front of depot. Kansas City."

Waterman home, a 10-room frame house at 702 Pennsylvania. Mother Celestia and three sisters attended patients in the 12-bed renovated house and trained other nuns to care for the sick.

In 1872, a smallpox epidemic struck the city. Mayor Robert H. Hunt secured permission to locate a pest house on a federally owned island in the Missouri River, opposite the East Bottoms. In the 1880s, a fire destroyed the quarantine buildings, and the sandbar island became a part of the mainland. The health department moved the pest house to another sandbar island in the river opposite Bluff Street. That island washed away in 1887.

In May 1878, Kansas City established a new board of health. Mayor George Shelley appointed six physicians to the board: J.M. Wood, D.R. Porter, J.W. Caldwell, J.O. Day, J.D. Elston and A.B. Taylor. In August, the city passed an ordinance to include Shelley (as ex-officio president), the fire chief, the police chief, the city physician (as sanitary superintendent) and an additional sanitary assistant. The city also established a health department to deal with smallpox, yellow fever, malaria, scarlet fever, typhoid fever, dysentery, tuberculosis and other diseases.

In 1878, differences between competing charitable groups forced the state to abandon the Orphans' Asylum it had built just two years earlier at 31st and Locust streets. Originally built by the state for orphans of Confederate soldiers, it later became a general orphanage operating with funds from Catholic and other charitable contributions. The Little Sisters of the Poor purchased the property and established a home for elderly men and women.

Organized charitable giving in Kansas City traces its roots to the Provident Association which formed in 1880 with funds it raised by subscription. Soon it served as the official agent for dispensing the city's charity funds. The founding group, 16 of Kansas City's leading citizens, offered assistance to the "deserving poor" and attempted to "expose the unworthy." Theodore S. Case, M.D., served as founding president and George Nettleton as vice president.

Increasingly, new and encouraging medical advances toward the end of the 19th century prompted physicians to want to train other physicians in a university setting. Eighteen prominent Kansas City physicians attempted to create such a teaching environment in 1880

University Medical College faculty and students outside All Saints Hospital, next to the college at 10th and Campbell. Financial and operating difficulties forced All Saints to close. The college eventually bought the property and renamed it University Hospital.

Crowds surround Lathrop School after a cyclone in 1886. The school at 8th and May later became a hospital for the Missouri Pacific Railway and the Memphis Railroad.

John and Charlotte Campbell lived at 209 Campbell. Charlotte and Campbell streets, familiar roadways on Hospital Hill, derive their names from this couple. Their property later served as a railroad hospital.

when they chartered the first University of Kansas City. (There is no connection with the 1933 University of Kansas City which became UMKC in 1963.) John Westley Jackson, M.D. (father of Jabez N. Jackson, M.D., a future AMA president) became the driving force behind the movement. In 1881, the University of Kansas City Medical Department dedicated a new three-story building constructed for $12,000 at the southeast corner of 12th Street and McGee, where the Kansas City Public Library now stands. The new Medical Department occupied the second and third floors and rented out the first floor to retail establishments.

In the same year, a dental department affiliated with the Kansas City Medical College at Seventh and Washington. John King Stark served as the founding dean. The Dental Department originated from several proprietary units that operated under various names in earlier years. In 1885, a group of pharmacists and physicians organized the Pharmaceutical Department, and located with the Medical Department of the new University of Kansas City at 12th and McGee.

The 1880s brought other developments in the social fabric of the city, as residents began addressing some of the concerns of the era. In 1883, the Humane Society organized "to prevent cruelty to women, children and animals." In the same year, the Women's Christian Association (WCA) opened a home for needy women and girls and hired Dr. Avis Smith and several other physicians to provide medical care.

And in 1888, the real estate boom in Kansas City, which had escalated to astronomic proportions as land values sometimes doubled and tripled in a single day, ended. Land prices in the new additions to the city fell overnight. Speculators lost paper fortunes, and many of the additions went undeveloped for decades.

COLONEL ROBERT H. HUNT

Robert H. Hunt was born in Ireland and moved to the U.S. with his family in 1849 when he was ten. During the Civil War, he served in the Union Army as a colonel of an Illinois regiment. Soon after the war, he moved to Jackson County to enter the real estate business. He established an office at 602 Main and became a wealthy, prominent citizen. In 1872, Hunt became mayor. His administration prospered, but a smallpox epidemic the first year he was in office killed many citizens. Since the city did not own a quarantine building, and no neighborhood would allow the city to establish a permanent pest house, Hunt faced a perplexing problem. The *Kansas City Journal*, in its July 18, 1887 issue, recalled the solution:

"At that time there was a large island in the Missouri River directly opposite the distillery, in the East Bottoms, one that was evidently not of rather recent origin, for it was covered with trees of large growth, while the soil had become rich enough to be successfully cultivated. It lay at no great distance from the shore, and the water between it and the main land was very shallow. Indeed at times the island was approachable by land, owing partly to a low stage of water and in part to the formation of extensive sand bars. The city concluded the island would be an excellent site for a pest house, but as it was claimed by parties owning adjacent land fronting on the river, the authorities were perplexed as to what course to pursue. In speaking of the manner in which the city finally secured control of the island, Colonel Hunt said:

'I wrote a letter to our member of congress, asking him to see if the island was claimed by the government. He investigated the matter and found that it had been reserved by the government for naval use. He succeeded in obtaining the consent of the government for the city to use it as a site for a pest house. At that time there was living on the island a man of the name of Menges. He had occupied it for years and refused to allow the city to take possession of it. There was urgent need for immediate action, so I decided upon a bit of strategy. I got all the material necessary for the pest house ready, and then invited Menges out to my house (Independence and Lydia), and while he was there the lumber was carried across the bridge, a structure which Menges had built, and by the time he returned, the small pox patients were in the hastily constructed pest house. That is how we obtained possession of the island, which was used by the city for several years, just how many I cannot now recall.'

"The island has now completely disappeared, and Colonel Hunt is of the opinion that it became a portion of the main land. The old pest house which stood upon it suddenly blazed out one night and lighted the river from shore to shore; next morning those who crossed the bridge found only a small heap of hot and smoking ashes on the site of the building. A few years later the city took possession of the island opposite Bluff Street, but during the high water of last month it was swept away by the current."

Col. Robert H. Hunt, real estate developer and city mayor during a smallpox epidemic in 1872.

19

1873 New York's Bellevue Hospital establishes the first modern American school of nursing.

1873 University of Missouri establishes a medical department in Columbia. Previously, from 1845 to 1855, a medical department existed in St. Louis.

1873 Financial panic country wide. U.S. economy suffers.

1874 University of Pennsylvania establishes the U.S.'s first university hospital.

1874 A.T. Still introduces Osteopathy in Kirksville, Missouri.

1875 New doctrine of Christian Science repudiates traditional medical concepts of disease and therapy.

1875 Missouri passes a "home rule" law for cities with more than 100,000 population.

1876 Meharry Medical College opens in Nashville, Tennessee.

1880 Homeopathic and eclectic medical

1870-1889

1870 Population of the City of Kansas: 32,286.

1870 City builds the first city hospital on present-day Hospital Hill.

1870 Two competing medical colleges merge.

1870 Nehemiah Holmes establishes the first horse-drawn streetcar line.

Nehemiah Holmes, founder of the first streetcar line and namesake for the main thoroughfare through Hospital Hill.

1870 Twyman: "'Rothlene' ... a form of scarlet fever."

1871 Twyman: "(S)ome pneumonia...intermittent fevers in the fall."

1872 Smallpox epidemic in the city.

1873 Nurses first serve in the city hospital.

1874 Grasshopper swarm.

1874 Twyman: "(V)ery dry and hot...sunstroke...diphtheritic croup...epidemic whooping cough."

1874 Fire destroys the 1870 city hospital.

1874 Sisters of Saint Joseph of Carondelet open a 20-bed hospital.

1875 Twyman: "(V)ery wet...capillary bronchitis among children...sore throat and catarrh among adults...some fatal cases of consumption."

1878 City passes an ordinance to create a Board of Health.

Dr. Isaac M. Ridge began his medical practice here in 1848. In the Civil War, he served as city physician, one of the few doctors left in town to treat the general populace. Ridge paid for the quarantine buildings Mayor R.H. Hunt ordered during the 1872 smallpox epidemic.

1879 First telephone exchange in Kansas City.

1880 Population of the City of Kansas: 55,785.

1880 Real estate boom in the city.

1880 Twyman: "Considerable sickness of a typo-malarial character...."

1880 City ordinance denies non-city indigent patients admission to the city hospital.

1880 A group of 18 physicians charters the first University of Kansas City Medical Department.

1880 Provident Association forms.

1881 First electric lights in Kansas City.

1881 Smallpox epidemic in the city.

1881 Formal reorganization of the modern-day Jackson County Medical Society.

1881 A Dental Department affiliates with the Kansas City Medical College.

1882 Kansas City Hospital College of Medicine opens.

1882 Members of St. Mary's Episcopal Church raise funds to establish a charity hospital.

The Rev. Nathan Scarritt, D.D., L.L.D, a Methodist minister, civic leader and entrepreneur, helped found the first University of Kansas City and served as regents' board president.

1883 Women's Christian Association (WCA) opens a home for the care of needy women and girls.

1884 First electric trolley car in Kansas City.

1885 Kansas City Episcopalian Church Charity Association founds All Saints Hospital.

1885 Pharmaceutical Department of the University of Kansas City forms.

1885 Wabash Railway hospital opens.

1886 A cyclone strikes Kansas City.

1886 German Hospital Association founds a private, non-sectarian hospital.

Dr. Flavel B. Tiffany directed a staff of four physicians when All Saints Hospital opened. Two decades later, he conceived a plan to build a health resort north of the city. He never built the spa, but a town, Tiffany Springs, just south of present-day Kansas City International Airport, remains today as a reminder of the plan.

1881   *sects proliferate in the U.S.*

1881   *Clara Barton, a nurse, organizes the American Red Cross.*

1881   *University of Pennsylvania introduces the entrance examination as a prerequisite for enrollment in its medical school.*

1882   *Robert Koch discovers the tuber-cle bacillus, the "consumption" or pulmonary tuberculosis germ.*

1884   *Development of the first dissolvable pill.*

1884   *Koch determines the bacterial cause of cholera.*

1884   *Discoveries of the diphtheria, tetanus, and pneumonia bacilli.*

1885   *First visiting nurse service begins in Buffalo, New York.*

1889   *Flu epidemic strikes the U.S.*

1889   *First use of sterile surgical gloves.*

1889   *Mayo Clinic opens in Rochester, Minnesota.*

1889   *Johns Hopkins Hospital opens in Baltimore.*

1887   Pest Island in the Missouri River washes away.

1888   St. Joseph's Orphan Asylum opens.

1888   Kansas City Homeopathic College opens.

1888   Real estate boom ends in Kansas City.

1889   New city charter changes name to Kansas City, Missouri.

1889   All Saints Hospital closes.

1889   Kansas City Homeopathic Hospital opens.

1889   Kansas City College of Pharmacy opens.

To obtain more space and avoid the influence of the medical school, Calvin Hewitt, D.D.S., second dean of the Kansas City Medical College Dental Department, obtained the franchise of the Kansas City Dental College and moved the college to the YMCA, then to a new building in 1893.

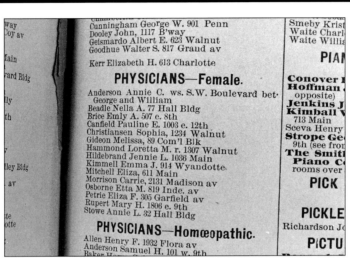

Several women physicians' names appeared in Hoye's 1887 City Directory. At the time, only Kansas City's home-opathic and eclectic medical colleges accepted female students.

21

In artist A. Ruger's 1879 bird's-eye view of Kansas City, Shawnee Avenue (subsequently Rosedale Road and now Southwest Boulevard) follows the Turkey Creek valley, upper right, to Kansas. The north-facing bluff of Hospital Hill appears at the upper left. View: NE to SW.

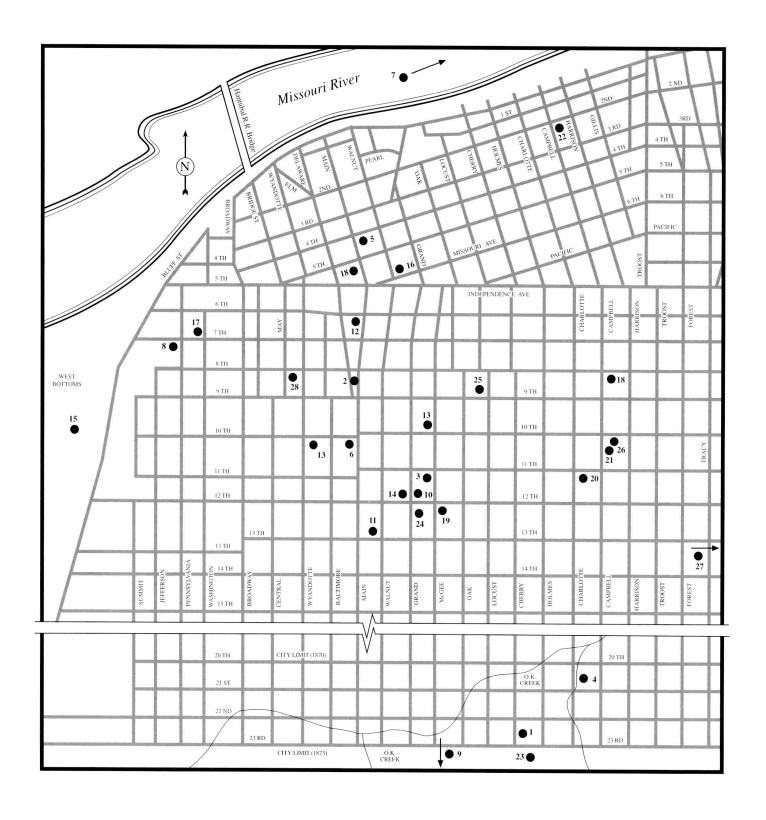

MAP KEY

1	1870	City Hospital, S of McGee's Addition.
2	1870	College of Physicians and Surgeons, Vaughan's Diamond or the Junction Building, junction of Main and Delaware at 9th.
3	1870	Women's Christian Association, SW corner of 11th and McGee.
4	1870	First Karnes School, E side of Charlotte, 20th to 21st.
5	1872	City Hall, SE corner, 4th and Main.
6	1872	College of Physicians and Surgeons Dispensary, 1002 Main.
7	1872	Pest-house island, Missouri River, opposite the East Bottoms.
8	1874	St. Joseph's Hospital, 702 Pennsylvania, SW corner of 7th and Pennsylvania.
9	1874	Widows' and Orphans' Home, Springfield Avenue (31st Street), Locust to McGee.
10	1875	Kansas City Surgical and Medical Institute, NE corner, 12th and Grand.
11	1876	Women's Christian Association, NW corner of 13th and Walnut.
12	1876	Dr. Payne's Kansas City Surgical and Medical Institute, 612 Main Street.
13	1877	Dr. T. W. Thornton: 1) 111 West 10th Street; 2) the future Thornton and Minor Hospital, 926 McGee, NW corner of 10th.
14	1877	Kansas City Surgical and Medical Institute moves to the NW corner of 12th and Grand.
15	1878	Union Depot, Union Avenue, West Bottoms.
9	1878	Little Sisters of the Poor, 31st and Locust.
16	1879	Kansas City Eye & Ear Infirmary, 551 Walnut, NE corner of Missouri Avenue and Walnut.
17	1880	Kansas City Medical College, 628 Washington, NW corner of 7th and Washington.
18	1881	K.C. Eye & Ear Infirmary moves: 1) to 546 Main, 2) then to 801 Campbell.
19	1881	University of Kansas City Medical Department, SE corner, 12th and McGee.
17	1881	Dental Department, Kansas City Medical College, 628 Washington.
2	1882	Kansas City Hospital College of Medicine, Vaughan's Diamond Building.
20	1883	WCA Children's Home, 1115 Charlotte.
21	1885	All Saints Hospital, 1005 Campbell.
22	1885	Wabash Railway Hospital, 209 Campbell.
19	1885	Pharmaceutical Department, University of Kansas City, SE corner, 12th and McGee.
23	1886	German Hospital, 2308 Holmes.
24	1888	Kansas City Homeopathic College, Schutte Building, 1209 Grand Avenue.
25	1889	Dental Department, Kansas City Medical College, fifth floor, YMCA building, NW corner of 9th and Locust.
26	1889	University of Kansas City moves to 911-913 East 10th Street, SW corner, 10th and Campbell.
27	1889	Kansas City Homeopathic Hospital, 1315 Lydia.
28	1889	Missouri Pacific Railway Hospital, SE corner, 8th and May.

Before his death in 1890, the Rev. Nathan Scarritt gave funds to establish Kansas City's first formal nurses' training school. In 1892, the Scarritt Bible and Training School for Missionaries and Other Christian Workers opened. The first floor contained nurses' quarters, offices, an operating room and classrooms. A self-sustaining hospital accommodated 50 patients on the second floor.

St. Joseph's Hospital established one of the nation's earliest nurse training programs, but it was not formally recognized until 1901. View: NE to SW.

University Hospital served as the training base for University Medical College. The sign on the frame house identifies the Eye, Ear and Nose Clinic. View: W to E.

A City Rises To Its Duty

In 1899, Drs. Alice Berry Graham and Katharine Berry Richardson moved with the Women's and Children's Hospital to larger quarters at 11th and Troost. Their Free Bed Fund Association offered 12 free beds instead of just one for children.

In 1904, Drs. Graham and Richardson converted a residence at 414 Highland into the 27-bed Mercy Hospital Association. View: SE to NW.

In 1887, the second pest-house island in the Missouri River washed away. Attempts to set up a new pest house brought angry protests from citizens. At first the city physician, one Dr. Sturdevant, on the advice of Mayor Henry Kumpf, attempted to set up storage tents for the salvaged pest-house equipment from the island. The tents were put on a vacant lot in Pendleton Heights, a Northeast neighborhood stretching from present-day Independence Avenue to Cliff Drive, Clairmont to Chestnut Trafficway. Residents of Pendleton Heights stormed the tents in fear that the city would take any inaction on their part as tacit approval for a permanent site. Their assault on the tentkeeper, who fended them off with a shotgun, probably represented the first NIMBY ("Not in my back yard") in the city. Next, the city attempted to locate a pest house on Raytown Road, south of the city, but again residents protested. City Ordinance No. 42693, approved in 1888, barred construction of a pest house "on the hill north of 2nd Street between Main St. and Grand Ave."

Eventually, in 1889, the city paid architect C.P. Schmidt $40 to design St. George Hospital, and passed Ordinance No. 285 to authorize $900 to build it. St. George Hospital turned out to be a boat docked at the foot of Cleveland Avenue, near Randolph Bridge. It burned in 1898, and although officials did not replace it, the city paid $22.95 in taxes on December 5, 1898 for John Bennett, who owned the land where the boat had docked. Later, the city maintained a small shack at the site, which it used infrequently during smallpox outbreaks.

By the 1890s, a plethora of new medical schools filled the pages of the city directory. One historian noted that only Chicago boasted "more medical schools than Kansas City." All were not legitimate, and some were not even formed specifically to teach medicine. For example, D'Estaing Dickerson, the third city physician, helped found the Kansas City Hospital College of Medicine in 1882 to oppose the city hospital's refusal to recognize the right of orthodox (allopathic) practitioners to consult with physi-

In 1898, Dr. C. A. Dannaker leased this home at 637 Woodland to establish the All Saints-Agnew Hospital and Training School for Nurses. The site is where the now-empty University of Health Sciences Hospital stands on Independence Avenue. View: W to E.

cians who had trained in other medical methods, specifically homeopathic and eclectic physicians. All three types, as well as others, trained at the Dickerson school, and several physicians graduated in 1883, but the Missouri Board of Health refused to issue certificates to them. The college threatened a lawsuit, and the state finally dropped the issue. Its point made, the college closed in 1888. In all, 53 physicians, 12 of them women, graduated from the Kansas City Hospital College of Medicine.

The Woman's Medical College began in 1895 in response to the refusal of the two allopathic schools to admit women. In the same year, the College of Physicians and Surgeons of Kansas City, Kansas opened; it later served as a medical department of the University of Kansas.

The opening of new schools continued at a fast pace, although few showed much imagination in creating distinct names. In 1896, the Kansas City University College of Homeopathic Medicine and Surgery became the medical department for Kansas City University, a second institution with this name, but in Kansas City, Kansas. The college admitted women and men on equal terms. Another Kansas school, the Kansas City College of Medicine and Surgery of Kansas City, Kansas, moved to Missouri two years later to be closer to teaching material and changed its name to the Medico-Chirurgical College. This school merged in 1905 with the University of Kansas. In July 1905, the University of Missouri in Columbia contemplated the acquisition of University Medical College. The Missouri curators sought a solution to their dwindling medical school enrollment and the lack of teaching material for the last two clinical years of its medicine program. The curators' offer to the college required a free hand to select the faculty of the Kansas City program, and complete control of a clinical hospital free from debt. University Medical College turned down the offer since it would probably mean loss of employment for the current faculty. In 1910, the University of Missouri dropped the last two years of its medical program. It would not become a four-year program again until 1956.

In the latter part of the 19th century, the United States recognized the practice of homeopathy, a system of medicine based on the fundamental principle that like cured like. When homeopaths found a drug to produce

The second site of Dr. John Punton's Sanitarium, later demolished. It catered to private patients with mental and nervous disorders, the first such institution west of the Mississippi. View: W to E.

Swedish Hospital opened in 1906 in this renovated residence at 1334 E. 8th Street. View: SE to NW.

Union Depot, completed in 1878 and second in size only to St. Louis's terminal, helped keep the West Bottoms crowded and dirty. The Blossom House, which had a reputation for more than overnight lodging, flourished on Union Avenue.

In 1891, City Hall housed the Emergency Hospital in its basement, much to the chagrin of local physicians. Police surgeons, instead of doctors at the city hospital, treated patients who needed emergency care. The emergency unit contained an operating room, three beds for females and eight beds for males.

the same symptoms as a certain disease, they used small doses of the drug to treat the disease. For example, homeopathic physicians believed that giving quinine to a healthy person caused the same symptoms that malaria did in a person who suffered from that disease, so quinine became the preferred treatment for malaria. In 1901, Kansas City Hahnemann Medical College, named for the founder of homeopathy, formed through the merger of the Kansas City Homeopathic Medical College (1888) and the Kansas City University College of Homeopathic Medicine and Surgery (1896).

At the same time that medical schools were expanding, hospitals had shed their almshouse image and had become acceptable places to receive medical care. More importantly, they had become necessary. Railroads built hospitals to care for sick or injured workers, usually transients or men away from home. The Kansas City, Fort Scott & Memphis Railway converted the old Wabash Railway medical unit at 3rd Street and Campbell into a larger facility, nicknamed Memphis Hospital. German Hospital had opened earlier to minister to patients mainly of German extraction and to impoverished immigrants who often spoke no English. Across town, members of St. Mary's Episcopal Church organized the Church Charity Association to raise funds and erect a free hospital, All Saints, for those in need in its congregation.

Because of the real estate bust and the movement of the rich to newer neighborhoods, houses glutted the Kansas City market in the late 1800s. Hospitals often renovated former residences, sometimes for a specific clientele or disease. Women's and Children's Hospital, under the guidance of Avis E. Smith, M.D., the first female physician to receive a medical license in Jackson County, offered only maternity and pediatric services. It began operation in a small house at Belt Line (15th Street) and Cleveland with furniture and equipment from the defunct Kansas City Maternity Hospital.

In 1897, two sisters, Alice Berry Graham, a dentist, and Katharine Berry Richardson, a physician, both in practice at the New (Isaac) Ridge Building, 617 Main Street, rented a bed there to care for indigent children. The work was supported through a Free Bed Fund Association they set up, separate from the hospital operations. Two years later, the hospital changed from a spe-

The original German Hospital (left) with dormitory (right) added for Sisters of St. Mary in 1902.

In 1895, German Hospital added this two-story wing (left) to its original facility (right).

In 1895, Isabella Brandon became the first graduate of the General Hospital Training School for Nurses.

Early construction on General Hospital's north wing, ca. 1905. View: NW to SE.

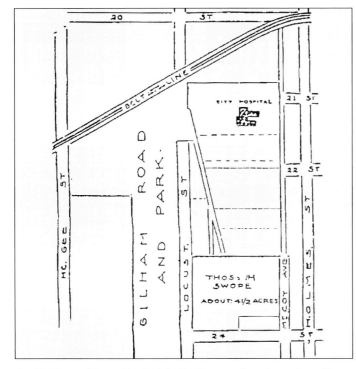

In 1903, architect Frederick C. Gunn relayed to city officials Thomas H. Swope's tentative offer of land for a city hospital.

cialized facility to a general hospital and moved to a three-story building at 11th Street and Troost.

In 1897, Dr. C. A. Dannaker's hospital career started with a borrowed bed in a single room at 14th Street and Pennsylvania. In September, he rented considerably more space for eight beds at 1220 E. 8th Street. In October 1888, he leased a home at 637 Woodland to establish All Saints-Agnew Hospital and Training School for Nurses, and worked out agreements with City Hospital, Memphis Hospital and Scarritt Bible School Hospital to offer nursing experiences there. The school graduated 53 nurses before it closed in 1909. In 1900, the Missouri Pacific Railway opened a new 30-bed hospital for railway workers in a 10-room house at 11th and Central, the former home of A. L. Mason. In 1904, Drs. Richardson and Graham established the first Mercy Hospital near Independence Avenue in the former residence of the niece of Col. Robert Hunt, the mayor who dislodged the squatter Menges from pest island in 1872.

Meanwhile, the city hospital had begun to show the wear and tear of years of use and makeshift repairs to its buildings and grounds. In 1895, the city had appropriated $25,000 for a second brick building (south) with a full basement for offices, an insane ward, a female ward and a surgical department. To accommodate the four-story addition, the city had razed one of the wooden structures used for smallpox patients. Two years later, the city authorized renovation of the 1884 (north) brick structure to include a new 150-seat clinical amphitheater, and in 1899, the city erected a one-story brick building with 45 beds for tubercular and contagious disease patients. The medical complex comprised three brick structures and one frame building, with a total bed capacity of 175. The city physician, also the surgeon-in-charge, managed the hospital with a house surgeon, two medical graduate assistants, a steward and nurses. In 1903, voters approved a $225,000 bond issue for a new municipal hospital. Col. Thomas H. Swope donated 4.5 acres of land — Gillham to McCoy, 23rd to 24th — worth $30,000, and Mayor James A. Reed accepted the gift for the city. Construction began on the north wing in 1905.

An operating room of the period at St. Joseph's Hospital.

West bluff north of 9th Street at the turn of the century. The squalor of the shanties on the hillside reflects the plight of the city's poor.

Dr. H. C. Carson advertised a Vitalized Home Treatment to cure cancer in his opulent Temple of Health at 1119 Washington on Quality Hill. Carson also advertised that he "gives no medicine." In 1907, Carson faced trial for practicing medicine without a license.

Kansas City Medical College added this building to its original complex at 628 Washington. View: E to W.

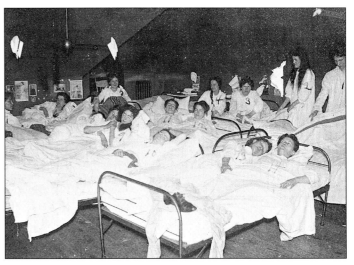

Although their images bear numbers, their identities have vanished from General Hospital archives. This photo vividly depicts a nurse's life at the turn of the century when, as historians later noted, students appeared to be "sleeping two and three in a bed" in the attic of Old City Hospital.

The new Convention Hall, northeast corner of 13th and Central, across from Bartle Hall, on the present site of Barney Allis Plaza. City officials used the building as a temporary hospital and shelter for victims of the 1903 flood.

The 1903 flood caused widespread damage and forced thousands of West Bottoms residents from their homes. Onlookers stood on the bluff at 11th Street to watch the old Union Elevator on fire. View: NE to SW.

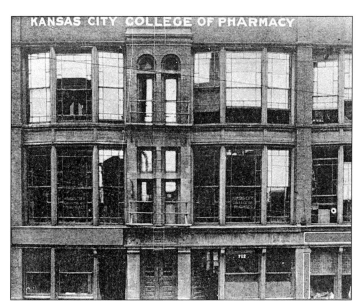

In 1897, a reincorporated Kansas City College of Pharmacy and Natural Science moved to rented quarters on the second and third floors of 712-14 Wyandotte, where it remained until 1923. View: E to W.

Medico-Chirurgical College on Independence Avenue between Campbell and Harrison, now part of the on-ramp of the 6th Street Trafficway. View: SW to NE.

In 1889, the Kansas City Dental College, on the northwest corner of 10th and Troost, added a third story.

The competing Western Dental College built this building in 1900 on the southwest corner of 11th and Locust, where City Hall now stands.

1890 Discovery of dental decay from bacteria.
1891 First diphtheria serum inoculation.
1892 Pettenkoffer's cholera theory proves the disease spreads through local groundwater and soil.
1893 Johns Hopkins Medical School forms in Baltimore. William Osler, M.D., introduces a close doctor-patient interaction concept.
1893 Initial discovery of insect-borne disease transmittal.
1894 Polio epidemic in the U.S.
1895 Discovery of the short-wave ray, or x-ray.
1895 Diphtheria antitoxin revolutionizes treatment.
1895 National Medical Association (African-American) forms.
1895 First satisfactory dental amalgam.
1895 Daniel David Palmer develops Chiropractic.
1896 First anti-typhoid inoculation.
1896 Nurses' Associated Alumnae of the United States and Canada forms.
1897 Discovery of the cause of dysentery.

1890-1907

1890 Population of Kansas City, Missouri: 132,716.
1890 Kansas City Academy of Medicine incorporates.
1890 Western Dental College opens at 12 West 10th.
1890 City appoints Thomas J. Pendergast superintendent of streets.
1891 Memphis Hospital buys Wabash Railway Hospital.
1892 Visiting Nurse Association (VNA) of Kansas City forms.
1892 Kansas City Dental College establishes an alumni association.
1893 Devastating flood in Kansas City inundates Armourdale.
1894 General Hospital organizes the Kansas City Training School for Nurses.
1894 College of Physicians and Surgeons forms in Kansas City, Kansas.
1896 Colonel Thomas H. Swope donates 1,324 acres for a city park.
1896 Crittendon Mission opens.
1896 Women's and Children's Hospital forms.

34

Alice Berry Graham, D.D.S., Richardson's sister and Mercy Hospital co-founder, headed the Free Bed Fund For Deformed and Crippled Children, a financial base that nourished the early Mercy hospital.

Katharine Berry Richardson, M.D., co-founder of Mercy Hospital, and one of the first female members of the Jackson County Medical Society. Today a Kansas City school at 3515 Park bears her name.

1896 Kansas City University College of Homeopathic Medicine and Surgery forms.
1896 B.C. Hyde, M.D., serves as police physician and surgeon.
1897 Kansas City annexes Westport.
1898 Thomas Swope donates land for the Gillis Orphans' Home and the Armour Home for the Aged.
1898 Eclectic Medical University forms.
1898 St. George Hospital, the city pesthouse boat for smallpox patients, burns.
1899 City builds Convention Hall for the 1900 national Democratic Convention.
1899 WCA builds the Gillis Orphans' Home.
1899 Homeopathic Hospital and Training Center for Nurses opens.
1899 University Medical College purchases the former All Saints Hospital.
1899 Associated Charities forms from several voluntary associations.
1900 Population of Kansas City: 163,752.

1900 Nettleton Home for Aged Women forms.
1901 Kansas City Hahnemann Medical College forms.
1902 Church Charity Association opens Saint Luke's Hospital.
1903 A devastating flood strikes Kansas City.
1903 Womans' Medical College at 13th and Grand closes.
1903 Joseph Walter Home opens at 2610 Cleveland Avenue. F. J. Hatch, physician-in-charge.
1903 Central College of Osteopathy forms.
1904 Armour Home for the Aged opens.
1904 Rest Cottage Rescue Home opens at 2033 Brighton.
1905 Missouri General Assembly grants city authority to condemn lands for hospital use.
1905 Mercy Hospital activates its nurse training school.
1906 Swedish Hospital forms.
1906 Tenement Commission forms to seek improvements in housing and sanitation in the city.
1906 Queen Esther Sanitarium opens at

Dr. Thomas C. Unthank helped found four black hospitals and served as a city physician to direct care of nonwhite victims of the 1903 flood.

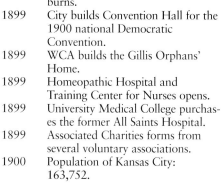

1898	Pierre and Marie Curie discover radium.	
1898	John Jacob Abel isolates epinephrin from adrenal glands.	
1900	Walter Reed Commission traces yellow fever to mosquito bite.	
1900	Karl Landsteiner divides red blood cells into three groups.	
1901	American Medical Association	reorganizes.
1901	First U.S. use of a blood-pressure cuff in surgery.	
1904	First use of Novocain in dental procedures.	
1904	A national association forms for the study of tuberculosis.	
1905	First dental hygienist.	
1906	First use of Wassermann test in the	diagnosis for syphilis.
1906	First federal Pure Food and Drug Act.	
1907	American Hospital Association (AHA) forms.	
1907	Missouri legislature passes a new Medical Practices Act.	

2634 Myrtle Avenue.

1907 Wesley Hospital opens.

1907 City establishes an 11-bed emergency hospital in City Hall.

1907 Kansas City Postgraduate Hospital opens.

1907 Eclectic Medical University moves to Kansas City, Kansas.

1907 Cornerstone ceremony for St. Mary's Hospital.

Drury Johnson McMillen, D.D.S., second dean of the Western Dental College (1890-1913), became wealthy from Kansas City real estate investments. McMillen built and owned the proprietary school at the southwest corner of 12th and Locust.

Mrs. David Whitmer established one of the earliest known central nursing directories in the country. This ad in a 1904 Kansas City Medical Index-Lancet urges clients to call "either phone" because two telephone companies, Bell and Home, operated in the city.

In 1905, surgery took place in a gaslit, radiant-heated amphitheater at University Medical College. The college replaced the demonstration room in 1908.

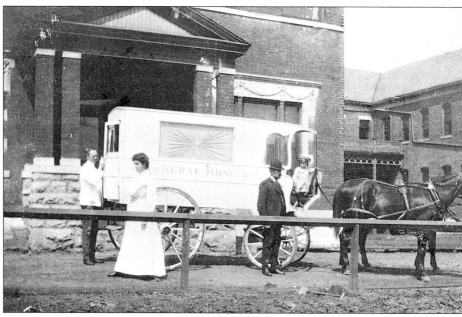

Frederick C. Gunn, architect of the 1908 General Hospital and former partner of famed Kansas City architect Louis Curtiss, originally designed the building during the tenure of Mayor James A. Reed (1900-03).

A horse-drawn ambulance in front of 2224 McCoy, before the move to the new General Hospital in 1908. Mechanized ambulances replaced horse-drawn vehicles in 1911.

36

Dr. Langsdale and day staff in front of City Hospital, ca. 1901-05.

GENERAL HOSPITAL

An 1894 photograph of the first brick building (1884) at City Hospital before a four-story brick addition in 1895. View: NW to SE.

Dr. John M. Langsdale, city coroner from 1890 to 1895, and surgeon-in-charge of General Hospital from 1901 to 1905. Langsdale founded the medical journal Langsdale Lancet *in 1896. It later merged with the* Kansas City Medical Index *under Dr. John Punton and became the* Kansas City Medical Index-Lancet.

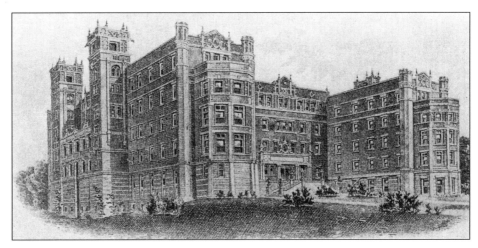

The final architectural rendering for the new General Hospital as it appeared in the 1909 Board of Hospital & Health Report.

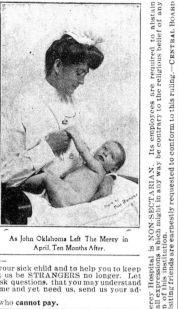

As John Oklahoma Entered The Mercy July 3rd.

As John Oklahoma Left The Mercy in April, Ten Months After.

DEAR MOTHER FROM A FOREIGN LAND:—
The Mercy wants to help you cure your sick child and to help you to keep your well child from getting sick. Let us be STRANGERS no longer. Let us be FRIENDS. Visit the Hospital. Ask questions, that you may understand all that you see there. If you cannot come and yet need us, send us your address and we will go to you.
All our beds are **free** and for those who **cannot pay.**

Visiting hours 2 to 5.—**ALL DAYS.** Out of town friends take notice.
We Urge a Visit.

Mercy Hospital is NON-SECTARIAN. Its employees are required to abstain from all expressions which might in any way be contrary to the religious belief of any patron of this institution. Visiting friends are earnestly requested to conform to this ruling.—CENTRAL BOARD

You have often said you wanted to help the Mercy. Do you, really? Then put this card into the hands of a poor Jewish mother who can read only Yiddish —or an Italian mother who only knows her own speech.
Rabbi Koplowitz and Mr. J. P. Deo have put our message in words that they can read.—Go take it to them.

[handwritten Yiddish text]

Mercy Hospital 414 Missouri & Highland

ITALIANI!!

CARE MADRI!
L'ospedale Mercy desidera di aiutare i vostri bambini di non cascare in malattie.
Venite al nostro Ospedale a farci visita onde tenerci in buona amicizia.
Venite qualsiasi giorno dalle 2 alle 5 P. M. domandateci qual sia questione che vi sia necessario.
Se avete bisogno di noi, e non potete venire, mandateci il vosto indirizzo che verremo noi da voi.
Tutti i letti del nostro Ospedale sono gratuiti, per quelli che non possono pagare.

Please Do Not Destroy This Card. Read It and Pass It On.

Patients and supporters called the early children's facility at 414 Highland "The Mercy". Mercy Hospital distributed this card to mothers and urged them to pass it on to others.

CHILDREN'S MERCY HOSPITAL

The Three O'Clock Passing. Each afternoon Mercy nurses passed out treats of homemade cookies, fruit or juice to their young patients.

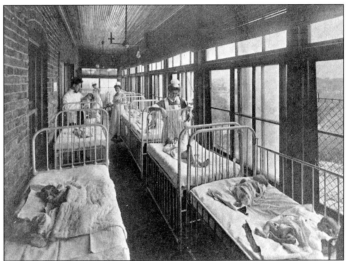

Babies in a back-porch ward at 414 Highland. Space was always precious at Mercy.

The chalkboard in front of the Mercy usually advertised the hospital's needs of the day. This message, however, solicited funds for a new hospital.

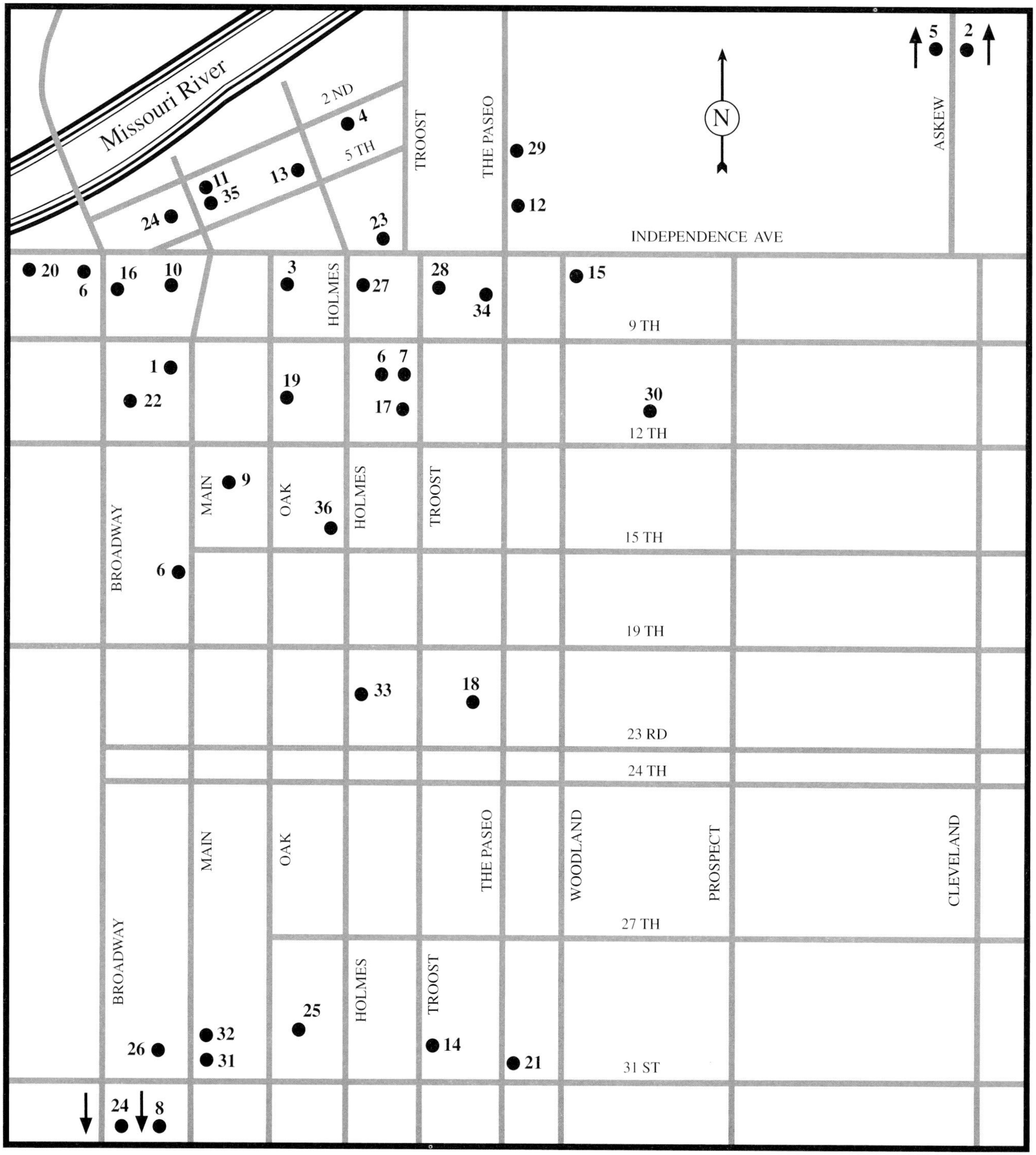

40

Missouri River

2 ND

THE PASEO

TROOST

ASKEW

5

2

4

29

12

11
35

13

24

5 TH

23

INDEPENDENCE AVE

N

20
6

16

10

3

HOLMES

27

28

34

15

9 TH

1

22

19

6 7

17

30

12 TH

MAIN

9

OAK

36

HOLMES

TROOST

15 TH

BROADWAY

6

19 TH

33

18

23 RD

24 TH

MAIN

OAK

THE PASEO

WOODLAND

PROSPECT

CLEVELAND

27 TH

BROADWAY

HOLMES

TROOST

25

32

26

31

14

21

31 ST

24

8

MAP KEY

1	1890	Western Dental College, 12 West 10th.
2	1890	St. George Hospital, riverfront, foot of Cleveland Avenue.
3	1890	Kansas City Homeopathic College, 421 East 6th.
4	1891	Kansas City, Fort Scott & Memphis Railway, 3rd and Campbell (Memphis Hospital).
5	1892	Scarritt Bible and Training School, Askew and Norledge.
6	1892	Kansas City Homeopathic College: 1) 504-506 West 7th; 2) 1618 Main; 3) 1020 East 10th.
7	1893	Kansas City Dental College, NW corner, 10th and Troost.
8	1893	Red Cross Hospital, Hunter Avenue (Linwood) and Wyandotte.
9	1895	Woman's Medical College, NE corner, 13th and Grand.
10	1896	Western Dental College, 716 Delaware, the Navajo Building.
11	1896	Crittendon Mission, 315 Main.
12	1897	Ralph Clinic, 529 Highland.
13	1897	Medico-Chirurgical College, 409-411 Cherry.
14	1897	Punton Clinic, SW corner, 29th and Forest.
15	1898	All Saints-Agnew Hospital and Training School for Nurses, 637 Woodland.
16	1898	Kansas City College of Pharmacy and Natural Science, 712-14 Wyandotte.
17	1899	Women's and Children's Hospital, NW corner, 11th and Troost.
18	1899	William Gillis Orphans Home, 2119 Tracy.
19	1900	Western Dental College, SW corner, 11th and Locust (present site of City Hall).
20	1900	Nettleton Home for Aged Women, 626 Pennsylvania.
21	1900	Punton Clinic, SE corner, 30th and Lydia.
22	1900	Missouri Pacific Railroad Hospital, 1031 Central.
23	1901	Medico-Chirurgical College, 918 Independence Avenue.
25	1901	Red Cross Hospital, 2828 Cherry.
6	1902	Kansas City Hahnemann Medical College, 1020 East 10th.
24	1902	St. Luke's Hospital, 427-29 Delaware; 4207 Central.
26	1903	Penn Valley Hospital, E side of Wyandotte at 30th.
27	1903	Kansas City Southern Railroad, 812-14 Harrison.
28	1903	Central College of Osteopathy, 729 Troost.
29	1904	Children's Mercy Hospital, 414 Highland.
18	1904	Armour Home for the Aged, 2125 Tracy.
30	1905	St. Luke's Hospital, 2011 East 11th.
31	1905	South Side Hospital and Training School for Nurses, 3007 Main.
32	1905	The Willows, 2929 Main.
33	1905	S.F.B. Morse School, SE corner, 22nd and Charlotte.
34	1906	Swedish Hospital, 1334 East 8th.
35	1907	Emergency Hospital, City Hall, 4th and Main.
36	1907	Centropolis Hospital, 1424 Holmes.
6	1907	Kansas City Postgraduate Hospital, 918 Independence.

General Hospital shortly after construction, before builders completed the south(west) wing in 1915. View: SW to NE.

This Baptist institution opened in 1908 and operated for many years at 620 Bennington. It later became Northeast Osteopathic Hospital. View: SE to NW.

A city bond issue passed to build a hospital exclusively for tuberculosis patients. Prisoners on the Municipal Farm, not exceptionally skilled, helped erect Leeds Tuberculosis Hospital under the architect's supervision.

CHAPTER FOUR

NEW HOSPITALS, HEALTH PROBLEMS AND MURDER MOST FOUL

German Hospital built its north wing in 1911. The previous buildings remained until 1915 to make way for the Bardon and South buildings. View: N to S.

Dr. John Edward Perry converted his home to a 16-room sanitarium, only the third hospital in the state devoted exclusively to the care of blacks. A two-story addition in the back served as kitchen and dining room. View: E to W.

S everal days before the new General Hospital opened in 1908, a reporter for *The Kansas City Star* described what the public could expect:

"The building is ready now for occupancy, except for a final sweeping out. Treatment there is free to the poor. It costs nothing to be sick at Kansas City's fine new hospital. The building has ten 'sun parlors' where convalescents may find relief from the melancholy 'atmosphere' of the various wards. In various parts of the hospital are the 'quiet rooms' for the patients who may be near death. Across the hall from the operating room in the clinical department is the 'recovery room.' It's the place where the patients will 'come to.' There they will do their laughing and weeping as they recover from the influence of chloroform or ether. The beds in the 'insane ward' have railings (and) are constructed so that a 'restraining sheet' may be fastened over the top when the patients become violent. All of the new beds are provided with comfortable springs. The nurses 'look-out' is never to be without an occupant who will keep vigilant watch over her ward. Each ward has a 'diet kitchen,' where nurses prepare delicacies for the patients. Cooks never enter the 'diet kitchens.' There the nurses make egg nog and toast, boil eggs and prepare special dishes suited to the patients' needs. As much care will be given to the preparation of the patient's food as the giving of the medicine."

The reporter went on to describe the building in detail:

"The building is five stories high, built of gray brick and laid with white mortar. The structure is fireproof . . . the floors are hardwood, laid on concrete and the window sills marble. Corners on the floors are round. Air is washed and dried before it enters the wards. The ventilating system is arranged so that it will not be necessary at any time to open a window; thus

43

When St. Vincent's Hospital opened in 1909, the Maryknoll Sisters offered the first obstetrical service in the city. The hospital later built an annex for infants, St. Anthony's Home, just east of the main building. View: SE to NW.

In 1895, the Sisters of St. Mary's Infirmary of St. Louis succeeded the Sisters of St. Francis as nurses at German Hospital. In 1904, St. Mary's recalled the nurses; in 1909, St. Mary's completed its own 200-bed hospital with an entrance at 28th and Main. View: NE to SW.

drafts will be avoided. The wards will have a constant supply of pure air at the desired temperature. Two fans, sixteen feet in diameter will pump 57,000 cubic feet of air into the building. In summer time the air will be cooled and in winter it will be heated. The hospital has an ice plant . . . electric light plant . . . a complete laundry . . . two electric elevators . . . and a private switchboard (for) thirty-two telephones."

When the city completed General Hospital in 1908 the cost stood at $481,437, more than double the original $225,000 bond issue of 1903, an overrun the city paid with general revenue funds. Under a new city charter that year, all hospital departments came under the control of a newly formed Hospital and Health Board. Members included Charles Armour, Edward F. Swinney, E.L. Martin and health commissioner Walter S. Wheeler. Thomas T. Crittenden, Jr. served as ex-officio president and J. Park Neal as acting hospital superintendent. In 1909, at a City Council meeting, the issue of homeopathic care versus allopathic treatment at the hospital surfaced. Hahnemann Medical College officials from the local homeopathic institute threatened a lawsuit to require the hospital to provide 25 percent of the patients' homeopathic service, literally life blood for its program. The controversy dragged on until September 1911 when the board ruled that no members of the various medical school faculties could conduct patient care clinics at the municipal facility as they had in the past. University Medical College, which had experienced financial difficulties and now offered just the last two years of clinical work in its training, claimed the decision would cripple the college. Hahnemann faced lower enrollments as the public's interest in homeopathic medicine declined. Both University Medical College and Hahnemann would close within four years, victims of an epidemic of another kind, the findings of the Flexner Report on Medical Education in the U.S. and Canada that criticized most of the nation's medical colleges as inadequate training institutions.

Another issue, that of charges of inhumane treatment of patients at the new Kansas City General Hospital, arose in 1912 but proved to be nothing more than a political ploy to embarrass the hospital administration.

When hospital officials moved patients from Old City Hospital to the new building in 1908, they left

Colored Division, Kansas City General Hospital. View: E to W.

St. Margaret's Hospital in Kansas City, Kansas did not allow female medical students from the University of Kansas to train there. They trained instead at General Hospital.

When Grace Hospital opened in July 1912 in the building to the right, it was only five stories high. In 1928, the Evangelical Deaconess Society acquired it and commissioned architects to enlarge it. This architectural rendering of the proposed additions shows extra stories on the original Grace Hospital (right of the arrow) and a new nine-story building to the left (west) on an alley corner between Harrison and Campbell. View: SE to NW.

This sewer pipe emptied its septic and surface sewage into O.K. Creek. In its 1912 Report on Housing Conditions, the Board of Public Welfare described the creek as a "stream of filth."

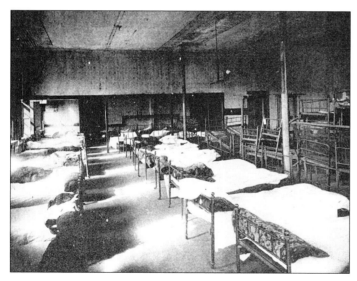

Interior of a typical dormitory lodging house. Their prevalence in the city prompted the report to note a "strikingly large population of homeless men . . . prone to contagious disease." Cost for a flophouse bed: 10 to 20 cents a night.

black and Hispanic patients behind to create a segregated city hospital for the first time. White physicians remained to treat nonwhite patients under the direction of George P. Pipkin, M.D., who had been in charge of the string of city pest houses the hospital had run since 1890. The medical staff, however, included four black physicians, among them Dr. Thomas C. Unthank, who had established Douglass Hospital in Kansas City, Kansas, the first black hospital west of the Mississippi, and who had served the city well during the 1903 flood. Dr. Unthank had urged authorities to use Old City Hospital as a training school for black physicians and nurses. In 1911, the city approved the idea, opened a school of nursing, accepted the first black intern and appointed a black doctor, William J. Thompkins, superintendent. General Hospital #2 and its school of nursing then became the first black, professionally managed hospital in the country. In August the following year, 14 visiting medical and surgical staff from General Hospital #1 charged that the new black interns at #2 had failed examinations for internships. A later investigation proved the charge false.

In 1903, a Texas-born graduate of Meharry Medical College in Nashville and a former physician in Columbia, Missouri, Dr. John Edward Perry, arrived in town. Appalled at the state of medical care for black citizens and eager to open a hospital to train other black men to become physicians, he established the 14-bed Perry Sanitarium in his Kansas City home in 1910. He later became the first superintendent of Wheatley-Provident Hospital, an outgrowth of the sanitarium. Wheatley founders dedicated the hospital in the name of "Negro citizens of Kansas City."

Several voluntary organizations, proprietary groups and local governments began to open hospitals and institutions of care to serve specific purposes or clientele: St. Mary's Hospital, St. Vincent's Maternity Hospital, Red Cross Hospital (as a training hospital for nurses), the Volker Tuberculosis Pavilion north of Old City Hospital, the Jackson County Home, the Leeds Tuberculosis Hospital, East Side Hospital and St. Anthony's Infants' Home.

Despite the greater access to hospital care early in the 20th century, a report in 1912 showed graphically that the city needed to work more on health issues. The report, issued by the recently created Board of Public Welfare,

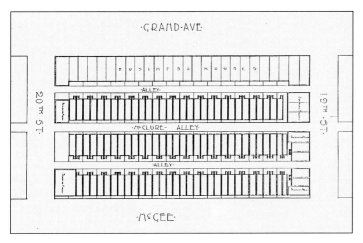

The Report on Housing Conditions cited McClure Flats, four blocks south of Hospital Hill, as an example of over-crowded housing.

McClure Flats. Businesses fronted on Grand; one row of houses fronted on McGee, while two rows of houses faced one another in McClure Alley.

The Report on Housing Conditions stated the "most evident evil in connection with our city housing is the privy vault." This tenement backyard featured a common-use, double-deck privy vault as well as a barnyard. The Welfare Board recommended sanitary removal of human waste to avoid the spread of typhoid fever.

Many tenements lacked city water and proper toilet facilities. There were almost 50,000 buildings in the city, but only about 20,000 used running water. City sanitary squads made home visits to teach sanitation principles.

condemned sanitation guidelines for the city. The *Report on Housing Conditions in Kansas City, Mo.* recommended amendments to proposed new building codes for the city. The board had studied six districts, from the Missouri River to 31st Street, and from State Line east to an irregular boundary of Woodland from the river to 8th, west to The Paseo, then south to 18th, west again to Holmes until it met the Kansas City Terminal Railway tracks, then south on Main and Wyandotte to 31st Street. Under a section entitled *Some Existing Evils in Kansas City Housing*, the report stated: "The most evident evil in connection with our city's housing is the privy vault." In other words, the outdoor toilet.

"In the Penn Valley district," the report continued, "inhabited by working men and their families — substantial, every-day, you-and-I-kind of people — there are 1,179 dwellings. The toilet facilities are . . . Modern, 200; dry sewer connected, 439; vaults, 530. (O)nly 17.11 percent of the total toilet facilities are modern." Of the privy vault, the report stated: "Sanitary science is agreed that typhoid fever is bound up with the presence of vaults. The common house fly does the damage. Wallowing on the top of decaying fecal matter, the fly begins its journey to the screen door of the house near or far. Your neighbor's flies are not concerned with confining their visits to your neighbor's house."

Of Quality Hill, which by 1912 essentially was a rooming-house district, the report stated: "In twelve to fifteen years a complete transformation has taken place. Owing to the encroachment of business and changes . . . a metamorphosis as distinct as that from the caterpillar to butterfly has taken place, with the difference that it has been a butterfly to caterpillar change rather than a caterpillar to butterfly change."

The section of O.K. Creek sewer at its mouth in 1912.

Plans for Union Station required the submergence of O.K. Creek in sewer tunnels that would run under the station and connect with Turkey Creek on the station's west side.

West Portal of the O.K. Creek sewer at 25th and Penn Street.

In 1915, before the completion of the tuberculosis hospital at Leeds, patients lived in this tent colony on the grounds.

DR. HYDE AND MR. SWOPE

When Thomas H. Swope, a lifelong bachelor, died October 3, 1909, he left an estate of $3.5 million and a reputation as a generous man. In fact, Swope's gift of 1,324 acres for a public park was the largest gift of land Kansas City has ever received.

Thousands passed Swope's casket in a public funeral at the city library a week after his death. But they couldn't have known that Dr. Bennett Clark Hyde, husband of Swope's niece Frances, allegedly administered a poison capsule to Swope the night of his death. Or that three days before, Swope's cousin and business manager, Col. James Moss Hunton, also had died suddenly in the Swope household. Hyde's diagnosis in both cases: apoplexy. Over the next few weeks every member of the Swope family at home, as well as several employees, fell ill from typhoid fever. Although Dr. G. T. Twyman (Leo's grandson) cared for the family regularly, Hyde usurped Twyman's role for a reason.

In June 1905, Hyde and Frances Swope had eloped. Frances Swope's uncle and her mother opposed the marriage because Hyde had garnered a reputation around town as a philanderer. About two years later, however, during an illness Hyde suffered, the Swopes and Hyde reconciled. In fact, Tom Swope later informed Hyde about his will; he had

In 1866, three weeks after he arrived in the Town of Kansas, Thomas Hunton Swope bought 30 acres of land for $7,500. His speculative purchase ran from Main to beyond McGee, from 9th to 12th, the heart of the city of the future.

made generous bequests for all Swope family members, but had not yet decided how to dispose of a residuary amount of $1.4 million. When Hunton, who was Swope's executor, died, Hyde immediately began a campaign to become executor, even asking Swope's nurse to help with the plan. The fewer Swopes that survived, the larger the estate would be for Hyde's wife, Frances.

Hyde's undoing came when a bacteriologist who had provided typhoid germs for Hyde as a culture became suspicious of the epidemic at Swope Place. Next, Margaret Swope, a niece, and others suffered seizures. On December 6, Chrisman Swope, a nephew, died. The nurses attending the Swope family convinced Dr. Twyman that Hyde had caused the deaths by poison. Twyman confronted Hyde with the allegations, and some members of the Swope family later testified they had witnessed Hyde disposing of cyanide capsules. Hyde promptly left Swope Place with Frances, never to return. On January 10, 1910, autopsy experts in Chicago examined Thomas Swope's exhumed body. When they found Hyde's cause of death incorrect, *The*

When Bennett Clark Hyde, M.D., married Swope's niece Frances, his career as a physician escalated. In 1908, he received a staff appointment in surgery at General Hospital, and two years later Jackson County Medical Society members elected him president.

Frank Walsh, defense attorney for Bennett Clark Hyde, held high civic and philanthropic posts in such organizations as the Board of Public Welfare and the Society for the Prevention of Tuberculosis. He went on to national prominence in New York and became an intimate friend of Gov. Franklin D. Roosevelt.

James A. Reed's reputation as a combative Jackson County and Kansas City prosecutor earned him accolades. He served two terms as mayor of Kansas City, three terms as a U.S. senator and twice was a presidential candidate. Reed served as special prosecutor in the first Swope murder trial. His name survives today as that of an eastside street, James A. Reed Road.

A bachelor, Thomas H. Swope lived with his widowed sister-in-law and her eight children in Swope Place in Independence.

Kansas City Star broke the story, and a grand jury soon indicted Hyde for murder. Somehow the jury transcript quickly became public knowledge.

The Swope family retained James A. Reed, a Pendergast "Goat," as special prosecutor. Hyde hired Frank Walsh, a Shannon "Rabbit," to defend him. The two attorneys had faced one another a decade before when Jesse James Jr., son of the famous outlaw, was tried for train robbery (James was acquitted). They would face each other again after the Hyde trial in the famous contempt-of-court case against *The Kansas City Star* publisher William Rockhill Nelson. But the Hyde trial represented the zenith of their legal careers.

The jury found Hyde guilty and recommended life in prison. Walsh appealed, and the Missouri Supreme Court reversed the decision. Hyde went through two more trials over the next seven years, one ending in a mistrial and the other a hung jury. Hyde lost his practice and for a while drove a truck for a living. Frances divorced him in 1921. He moved to Lexington, Missouri, practiced medicine for awhile, and died of a heart attack in 1934 at the age of 62. Hyde never served his term as president of the Jackson County Medical Society.

STRYCHNINE FOUND IN THE STOMACH OF COL. SWOPE NOT GIVEN HIM BY NURSE

Attendant, in Sworn Statement, Says She Refused to Give Philanthropist Hypodermic Injection Shortly Before Death; Other Organs of Civic Benefactor Are Being Analyzed.

(By FRANKLIN HARPER.)

(Special Representative of The Kansas City Post.)

CHICAGO, Jan. 21.—The strychnine found in the stomach of Col. Thomas H. Swope was not administered to him as a medicine before he died.

The last medicine given Col. Swope was administered by the nurse ten hours before his death.

The nurse who was attending Col. Swope in his last illness has made a sworn statement, and that statement is here, that she was ordered to

1909   *Freud and Jung lecture in the U.S.*
        on psychoanalysis.
1909   *First typhus vaccine.*
1910   *University of Missouri discontin-*
        ues the last two clinical years of
1910   *its medical program in Columbia.*
1910   *Carnegie Foundation publishes*
        the Flexner Report on Medical
        Education.
1910   *Chemist Paul Ehrlich discovers a*
1911   *cure for syphilis.*
1911   *First use of the word vitamin to*
        describe essential chemicals in the
        diet.
1912   *Introduction of phenobarbital as*

1908-1915

1908   New city charter establishes a
        Hospital and Health Board that
        includes three lay members.
1908   William Volker helps found the
        first city-level public welfare
        board in the U.S.
1908   Allen Medical and Surgical
        Institute and Eye Infirmary opens
        at 27th and Colorado.
1909   Mercy Hospital completes a 50-
        bed addition at 414 Highland.
1909   St. Mary's Hospital opens.
1909   St. Vincent's Hospital opens at
        3210 East 23rd.
1909   Missouri enacts licensure legisla-
        tion for nurses.
1909   South Side Hospital changes from
        a private to a public facility.
1909   Red Cross Hospital changes from
        a private to a public facility.
1909   Western Eclectic College of
        Medicine and Surgery returns to
        Kansas City, Missouri from
        Kansas City, Kansas and resumes
        its former name, Eclectic Medical
        University.
1909   City inaugurates a public schools
        medical-inspection program.
1909   City opens a tuberculosis unit at

John Edward Perry, M.D., a Meharry Medical College graduate, served as a medical officer in the Spanish-American War, then practiced in Columbia, Missouri, from 1899 till 1903 when he moved to Kansas City. In Kansas City, Perry worked to obtain specialized training for black physicians, first at his own sanitarium and later at Wheatley-Provident Hospital.

        22nd and Cherry, a gift from
        William Volker.
1910   Population of Kansas City:
        248,381.
1910   Jackson County Home, Patterson
        Hall, opens.
1910   St. Teresa's Academy moves to
        5600 Main.
1910   City passes a bond issue to fund a
        TB hospital at Leeds.
1910   Swedish Hospital graduates its
        first nursing student.

1910   G. Wilse Robinson, M.D., leaves
        the superintendency of GH #1 to
        assume ownership of the Punton
        (Psychiatric) Clinic.
1911   Swedish Hospital purchases the
        former Penn Valley Hospital.
1911   The county home, Patterson Hall,
        changes its name to the Jackson
        County Home for the Aged and
        Infirm.
1911   German Hospital opens a new
        125-patient facility at 2300
        Holmes.
1911   Saint Luke's Hospital Club opens
        a summer baby camp at Missouri
        Avenue and Charlotte.
1912   East Side Hospital Association
        opens a 25-bed private, general
        facility at 920 Newton Avenue,
        near the Belt Line. A. B.
        Mulvaney, medical superinten-
        dent.
1912   Mabel E. Gammage Memorial
        Hospital opens at 4800 East 24th.
        T. R. Gammage, physician-in-
        charge.
1913   German Hospital establishes the
        first department of radiology in
        the city.

a sedative.

1913　*First isolation of amino acids from blood.*

1914　*World War I begins.*

1914　*Pasteurization of milk begins in major U.S. cities.*

1914　*AMA publishes first list of approved hospitals for intern training.*

1913　Dr. Alice Berry Graham, co-founder of Mercy Hospital, dies.

1913　University Hospital Training School for Nurses opens at former University Hospital.

1914　Dedication of Union Station at 24th and Main.

1914　Mercy Hospital establishes a board of trustees.

1914　Perry Sanitarium incorporates as the Provident Hospital and Nurse Training Association.

1914　St. Vincent's Hospital begins construction of St. Anthony's Home For Infants, which connects with the hospital.

1915　GH #1 opens a 40-cot children's ward, ostensibly to relieve Mercy Hospital of some of its obligations.

1915　JCMS attacks the city hospital administration in a series of editorials in its *Weekly Bulletin*. Criticisms continue into the 1920s and 1930s.

1915　Saint Luke's builds an addition to its 11th and Euclid facility.

1915　Tuberculosis Hospital at Leeds opens.

1915　Hahnemann Medical College on 10th Street changes its name to Southwest School of Medicine and Hospital, but closes the following year.

1915　An offshoot of the Eclectic Medical University, the Kansas City College of Medicine and Surgery opens at 2225 Holmes.

Medical colleges in the city often competed for fresh cadavers for dissection from local cemeteries.

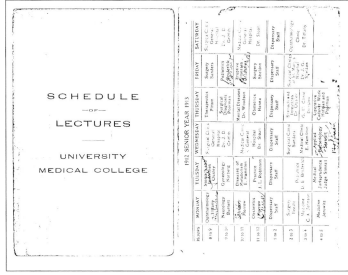

Unfortunately for underclass members, University Medical College closed in 1913.

Nurses' dormitory room at University Medical College. Thirty-seven nurses enrolled in the training program in 1909. Entry required a high school diploma and written references; students served a two-month probationary period.

The free dispensary offered a variety of clinics: surgery, general medicine, dermatology, women's diseases, neurology and psychiatry, obstetrics, pediatrics, laryngology and rhinology. In 1907-08, students and their instructors, without compensation, treated 19,417 patients.

UNIVERSITY MEDICAL COLLEGE

This ad appeared in the University Medical College yearbook, The Scalpel. *Faculty members included some of the city's premier physicians.*

University Medical College,

909, 911 and 913
East Tenth St.,

KANSAS CITY, MO.

CLINICAL FACILITIES
UNSURPASSED.
LABORATORIES THOROUGHLY
EQUIPPED.

THE HOME OF
"THE SCALPEL."

J. M. FRANKENBURGER, M.D., Secretary,
Rialto Building, Kansas City, Mo.; or

JAMES E. LOGAN, M.D., LL.D., Dean,
1208 Wyandotte St., Kansas City, Mo.

55

Instructors held a general clinic each week in the new demonstration operating room.

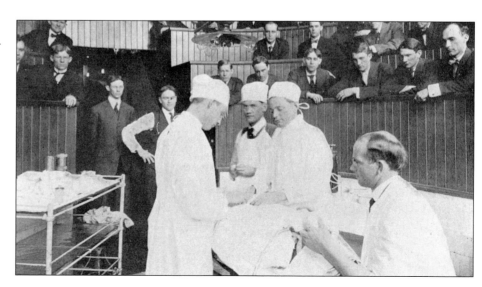

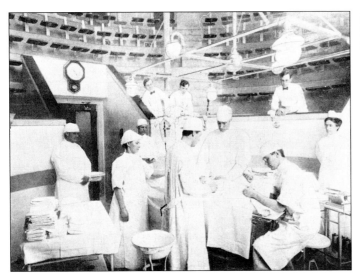

As the only operating room at General Hospital, the fourth-floor amphitheater proved inadequate. Surgeons sometimes began an operation as another procedure ended, and often used an anesthesia anteroom for minor operations.

To handle scarlet fever, diphtheria and measles, the Hospital and Health Board authorized in 1910 an isolation hospital for children. The structure did not connect with the main hospital, contained no elevators and also proved inadequate.

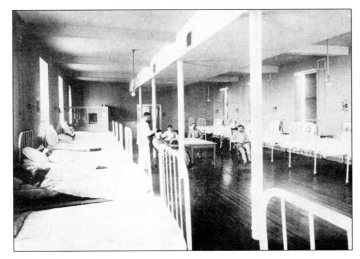

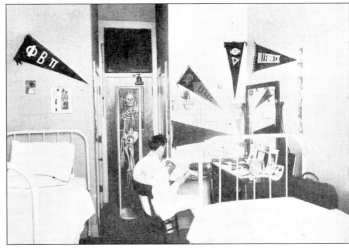

The third floor accommodated patients on all services.

Interns lived on the fourth floor of the north building.

GENERAL HOSPITAL

Nurses wore probationary uniforms
during their early training.

Most prominent physicians of the time volunteered their services.

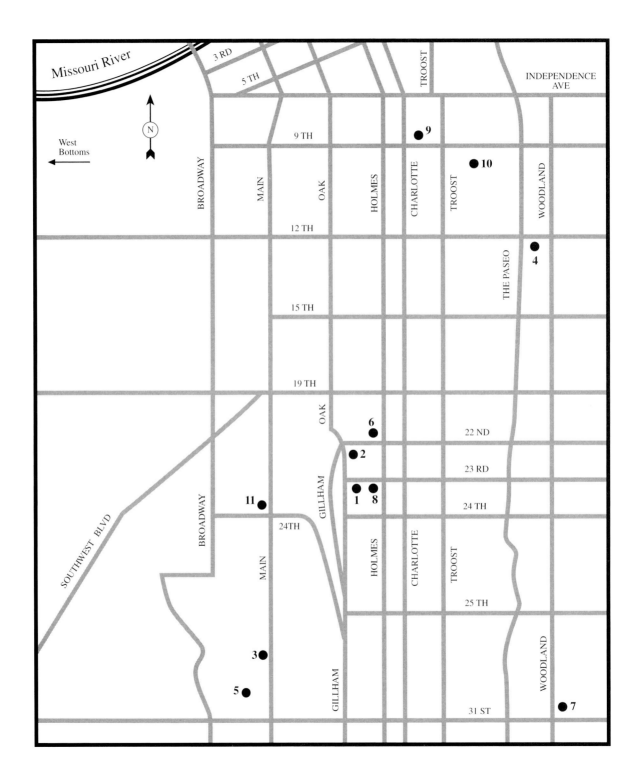

58

MAP KEY

1	1908	General Hospital, 23rd and Cherry.
2	1909	Kansas City Tuberculosis Pavilion, 22nd and Cherry.
3	1909	St. Mary's Hospital, 28th and Main.
4	1910	Perry Sanitarium and Nurse Training Association, 1214 Vine.
5	1911	Swedish Hospital, W side of Wyandotte, at 30th.
6	1911	General Hospital #2, Old City Hospital, 2104-14 McCoy.
7	1911	Florence Crittenton Home, 3001 Woodland.
8	1911	German Hospital, SW corner, 23rd and Holmes.
9	1912	Grace Hospital and Training School for Nurses, NW corner, 9th and Harrison.
10	1913	Hahnemann Hospital, 912 Tracy.
11	1914	Kansas City Terminal Railway Hospital, upper floor, W wing, Union Station, 24th and Main.

In 1911, lumber magnate R. A. Long subscribed $400,000 to build the distinctive yellow-brick Christian Church Hospital at 27th and The Paseo. Charity patients occupied the second floor, with women on the south end, men on the north. The building at the right housed the nurses' residence. View: SW to NE.

Research Hospital had completed most of its Hospital Hill construction by 1918. This view, SW to NE on McCoy (Kenwood), displays a different view of the South and Bardon additions of the previous year.

60

In 1918, Wheatley-Provident Hospital and Nurses' Training Association opened at 1826 Forest in the former St. Joseph's Catholic Parish elementary school. View: W to E.

Vineyard Park Hospital, a 50-bed osteopathic facility, opened in 1920 across the street from what is now the UMKC School of Dentistry. The hospital maintained a separate fund for charity work it performed, and later renamed itself Doctor's Hospital. The hospital closed in the early 1970s and demolished the building. View: NW to SE.

CHAPTER FIVE

1916-1929

MORE EPIDEMICS, WORLD WAR, POLITICS AND PATRONAGE

Swedish Hospital moved from its downtown location in 1911 when it purchased the former Penn Valley Hospital at 30th and Wyandotte. View: NW to SE.

In 1921, Swedish Hospital renamed itself Trinity Lutheran to avoid a public misconception that it treated only Swedish patients. The hospital converted the porches on the original apartment-like building to enclosed wards, and in 1925 dedicated a new $201,696 five-story building (right).

In three years, General Hospital had filled to capacity and had become hard-pressed to offer sufficient services for the growing Kansas City population. By 1913, an alarmed Jackson County Medical Society tried to address public concerns about the new city hospital. The Medical Society, in the April 5 issue of its *Weekly Bulletin*, wrote: "There is prejudice against the General Hospital in this community and this feeling is most prevalent among those who are most likely to need its services."

The editorial then offered some suggestions: "The Jackson County Medical Society should take the initiative in an active movement to change the public feeling. It is no longer necessary to stir up 'an indignation campaign' to correct some little lapse in the detail of the hospital management. The staff is chosen from the best specialists in the various branches of medicine . . . interns are keen young fellows from the best medical schools . . . nursing service is as good as the best . . . general equipment is as good as money can buy. A quiet talk with the proper official will either correct the error or convince one that no injustice is being done."

In defense of the hospital, the editorial offered this barb: "In view of these conditions many feel that the time has come to discourage semi-private hospitals which are calling on the public for help to sustain charity wards. These were necessary at one time but they have served their purpose. (If) an individual or group of individuals has the inclination and means to endow a hospital (they have) a perfect right to do so, but we feel that the general public should be relieved of further financial responsibility when it provides the best, as Kansas City has done. 'Tag Days' and 'Hospital Days' are no longer necessary."

Despite Medical Society concerns, several institutions and groups did have the inclination and means to endow hospitals. The city's "Hospital for the

Mrs. Annie Bird, wife of Emery-Bird-Thayer Dry Goods Company tycoon Joseph T. Bird, and their daughter, Josephine, wife of Porter T. Hall (a descendant of the Rev. James Porter), contributed property at 15th and McGee to help build Nurse Hall next to Children's Mercy Hospital. View: SE to NW.

William Volker contributed the funds to build the Research Hospital Nurses' Residence in 1927, presently the UMKC School of Nursing. View: SE to NW.

Little People," Mercy Hospital, held fundraising drives in 1915 and 1916 to build a new hospital on two acres of land on Independence Boulevard that Jemuel C. Gates had previously donated. R.R. Brewster, a lawyer and a trustee of Mercy, led the campaigns that obtained pledges from such large contributors as Robert A. Long, William Volker, Charles W. Armour, H.D. Lee and Cliff C. Jones.

Long, the lumber magnate who built the Northeast home that today comprises the main part of the Kansas City Museum, not only supported the new Mercy Hospital, but contributed heavily to the Christian Church Hospital at 27th and The Paseo, a Renaissance-style complex of cream vitreous brick. Long, a member of Independence Boulevard Christian Church, envisioned a complex of about a half-dozen structures on The Paseo for a variety of Christian Church charitable purposes. To reinforce the message of its mission, the church hospital devoted the second floor — a third of the beds — to charity patients. An interesting aside: in planning for the 1916 opening of the hospital, officials seriously considered calling it a sanitarium because of the stigma associated with the word hospital.

The Christian Church Hospital lasted 10 years, then closed because of internal strife. The original hospital building today stands vacant and in disrepair. The Veterans Administration occupied the hospital building for a few years while the Fairmount Maternity Hospital and St. Anthony's Home occupied the nurses' residence through the years. Welcome House, Inc., a working house for recovering alcoholics, now occupies it.

In 1916, sometime after black physician John Perry established the Perry Sanitarium, he enlarged it with assistance from the Provident Association, the city's clearinghouse for its charity funds. The official name became The Provident Hospital and Nurses' Training Association. When two black charitable groups, the Phyllis Wheatley Association — named for the famous Boston slave who became America's first important black poet — and the New Movement Association, attempted to establish another private hospital for blacks in the city, the Public Welfare Board encouraged them to unite in their efforts to support Perry's hospital. The two groups successfully incorporated as the Wheatley-Provident Hospital and Nurses' Training Association in March 1916. In 1918, the hospital moved to a renovated

Shortly after St. Luke's Hospital moved to 44th and Wornall, it completed this Nurses' Home in 1925 (demolished). View: NW to SE.

In 1917, German Hospital built this research laboratory near the main buildings, largely from funds provided by William Volker.

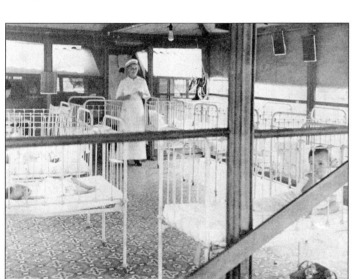

Summer Baby Camp at 21st and Jefferson, 1916. The camp, a charitable project of the St. Luke's Hospital Club, cared for sick babies with "disorders that go with summer." An electric fan cooled the tent; on rainy days nurses lowered side awnings to keep the camp "co(z)y and comfortable."

In 1919, the Emergency Hospital in the basement of City Hall moved to the fifth floor of the WalSix Building at 6th and Walnut. The unit served as a branch of City Hospital for the northside and as the city's charity dispensary. View: NE to SW.

Ernest Hemingway in 1918 in his Red Cross ambulance in France, shortly after he left The Kansas City Star *as a reporter on the short-stop run: General Hospital, Union Station, the weather bureau and the police station. Hemingway's 1933 short story about Kansas City General Hospital,* God Rest Ye Merry, Gentlemen, *impugns a flippant young doctor's medical ability in the emergency room.*

Catholic elementary school at 1826 Forest. Today that building stands vacant, except at Halloween when local promoters use it as a haunted house.

On November 11, 1918, when World War I ended, the world breathed easier. But that fall and winter a global influenza pandemic struck that eventually killed 20 million people, including more than 500,000 in the United States.

The influenza outbreak struck Kansas City as suddenly and disastrously as cholera had more than half a century before. First, 170 Army mechanic students who trained at Sweeney Automotive School, across from Union Station, came down with the flu in a 24-hour period, then 500 more in the next two days and 800 in the next week. Army mechanic students at another school, Rahe Automotive at 22nd and Gillham, suffered as well. The Army moved quickly to shut down its mechanic schools, and on October 7, A. J. Gannon, M.D., head of the city Health Department's contagious disease division, recommended a ban on all public gatherings. City health director E. H. Bullock, M.D., supported the decision, but irate business owners flagrantly disregarded the ban.

Gannon issued a second directive on October 17: "All theaters and motion picture shows, all schools and all churches must close. Public gatherings of twenty or more persons (private as well) are forbidden." Businesses with more than 20 employees could not open until 9 a.m. and were required to close by 4 p.m. After Gannon announced the second ban, William Motley, president of the Hospital and Health Board, reacted to pressures from business interests and Downtown politicians and fired Gannon in a wild meeting of insults between the two men. Bullock resigned as superintendent of General Hospital in retaliation, but remained as city health director. He then appealed to the U.S. Public Health Service for help. By the time two USPH officers arrived, the epidemic in Kansas City had subsided. During the last four months of 1918 the city lost 1,815 citizens to the epidemic from influenza and pneumonia.

In 1922, Dr. Katharine Berry Richardson, cofounder of Children's Mercy Hospital, solicited funds to start a pediatric clinic for black children at Wheatley Hospital. Children's Mercy offered only one bed with "no color line" for fear of losing contributions from its mainly white constituency. Richardson appealed to William Volker and Frank Niles for assistance to build

1918 Victory Celebration Arch in Union Station Plaza with Hospital Hill and the Rahe Automotive School in the background. Soon afterward, "Spanish Flu" would make such gatherings impossible.

Hospital Hill, ca. 1924, with the Kansas City Belt Line in the foreground. The city later built the Fire Alarm Exchange building on the bluff at the right. In the background: General Hospital, Research Hospital, two frame buildings of old City Hospital, houses on McCoy Street and the back of old City Hospital (#2). View: NW to SE.

By 1927, General Hospital had acquired a fleet of modern Lincoln and Ford ambulances, even a "sick car" for home visits, a practice the hospital continued until 1956.

Lou Gehrig, left, and Babe Ruth presented a refrigerator to Children's Mercy Hospital with proceeds from a benefit ball game in which Gehrig and Ruth played on Oct. 12, 1927 in Kansas City. Gehrig, the so-called Iron Horse of baseball, played in 2,130 consecutive league games before he fell victim at age 37 to amyotrophic lateral sclerosis (ALS), now known also as Lou Gehrig's disease.

a ward where black doctors could train and where black children could receive appropriate care. The two men contributed $74,000 for a two-story pediatric ward annex. Volker bought vacant land just north of Wheatley-Provident for $9,000, and he and Niles contributed an additional $65,000 to complete the 25-bed pediatric ward the following year. The hospital planned to add a nurses' residence on the north end of the addition, but never did.

In 1927, a fire at General Hospital #2 prompted city officials to replace the 57-year-old hospital with a proposed new $300,000 facility with funds from a city bond issue. Although most of the black community favored a site nearer their homes, on Michigan Avenue between 26th and 27th across from Spring Valley Park, an all-white group, the Linwood Improvement Association, opposed the location. The city eventually built the new General Hospital #2 on Hospital Hill next to the old General Hospital #2.

In the 1920s, the newly consolidated dental school, Kansas City-Western Dental College, encountered severe financial problems and the threat of losing its accreditation from the American Dental Association. Most proprietary schools — medicine, pharmacy, commerce, law and dentistry — suffered financially in the 1920s, and all looked toward affiliation with academic units of universities as a way to stay afloat. In 1926, the Methodist Episcopal Church accepted a gift of 147 acres at 75th and State Line to establish an institution with "Christianity at its heart." The donation came from Kate B. Hewitt, the widow of Dr. C. B. Hewitt, a former president of the Kansas City Dental College. Representatives of the church and the community appointed a board of trustees, and in December 1926, the trustees announced plans for a $5 million building campaign, along with a name for the university, Lincoln and Lee. In 1928, the dental college, an early affiliate of the new school-to-be, issued diplomas to its graduating class with the seal of Lincoln and Lee University, even though the school had not officially opened.

William Volker pledged $50,000 for the new university, by far the largest contribution. But later events would prove that he favored neither the school's affiliation with the Methodist Episcopal Church nor the location of the campus.

SOUTHEAST HOME PROTECTIVE ASSOCIATION

C. MURPHY, President

R. N. DeVault, Chr. Brooklyn Branch   Geo. Griffin, Chr., Bellefontaine Branch.   Wm. Eubank, Chr. Montgall Branch.

The Southeast Home and Protective Association, composed of the property owners in the Southeast District of Kansas City was organized for the following purposes:

1st, To protect white residence districts from the encroachment of Negroes.

2nd, To encourage the people to own their own homes, thereby creating a better class of citizenship.

3rd, To stimulate public and private improvements in the district and to protect home owners against unjust discrimination.

4th, To arouse an interest among tenants and owners of property in the appearance of their homes, the planting of trees, shrubs, and flowers and the care of yards and lawns.

This organization is NON-POLITICAL and NON-SECTARIAN and any white property owner, regardless of creed or party, who can endorse these principles may become a member.

We are determined that the district between Euclid and Benton and from 20th to 31st shall remain white territory and to this end our

Gummed Sticker Posted Where Negroes Can Read It

TO THE COLORED FOLKS:

We do not want you within these limits, SO STAY OUT. Why try to live in this district? . . (Signed) 50,000 East Side Residents.

organization shall hold as hostile to the best interest of the said district all persons who in any manner encourage, aid, or assist in any manner, the occupancy or ownership of property in this district, by Negroes.

That we recognize as belonging to such class as we term HOSTILE to the white people, the following among other classes of people.

1. Any owner of property offering to rent or sell property in this district to Negroes.

2. Any owner of property now renting property to Negroes in this district.

3. Any real estate dealer or agent, who in any manner whatsoever, lists for rent or sale to Negroes, any property situated in this restricted district.

4. Any agent, firm, company or broker or any other person who loans money or assists in obtaining loans on property to Negroes in this district.

5. Any insurance company, agent or broker who places or already having placed, retains or renews a policy of insurance on property in this district owner or occupied by Negroes.

We also ask that any real estate agent or broker handling property in this district now occupied by Negroes, be requested to place whites in said property and in the event that he refuses to do so, that he be considered hostile to the white interests of the district and the membership of this association and their friends withdraw from such agent their patronage and give it into the hands of some other agent.

Southeast Home and Protective Association.

By Secretary.

Southeast Home and Protective Association, with an obviously over-inflated membership total of 50,000, warned blacks to keep out of a neighborhood where the African-American community hoped to build the new General Hospital #2.

With Hospital Hill still segregated, the city in 1929 added a wing for black patients at the Leeds Tuberculosis Hospital.

1916   Discovery of heparin.
1917   U.S. enters the war against
        Germany.

1918   Worldwide influenza pandemic
        kills 20 million, 548,000 in U.S.
1921   Discovery of insulin for use in

        diabetes control.
1922   Discovery of Vitamin D, essential
        in children's diet for good health.

1916-1929

At the height of his power, Thomas J. Pendergast, Kansas City Democratic boss, controlled all aspects of city and county government. General Hospital employees, like many city and private workers, kicked back part of their wages or salaries to his political machine.

1916   Christian Church Hospital, 2625 The Paseo, opens. Marble covers the main entrance and the lobby, with the general finish of the building in oak. Future Mayor Ilus "Ike" Davis born there this year.

1916   Kansas City College of Osteopathy and Surgery opens in the New Center Theater Building at 15th and Troost.

1916   St. Teresa's Academy becomes a junior college.

1917   City adopts a community chest concept to help finance numerous charitable organizations.

1917   St. Joseph's Hospital moves to a new six-story, 250-bed facility at Linwood and Prospect.

1917   Largely from funds William Volker provides, German Hospital builds a research laboratory south of and adjacent to the main building.

1917   Central College of Osteopathy changes its name to Central College Medical Department which trains and graduates both medical doctors and osteopathic physicians.

1917   CMH moves one block from 414 Highland to its new location at 1710 Independence Boulevard.

1917   Smallpox epidemic in the city strikes

late in the year. City health authorities utilize the Leeds TB Hospital, closed several months for lack of funds, as an isolation unit for smallpox patients.

1918   March 14. German Hospital renames itself Research Hospital because of anti-German war sentiment.

1918   Many Kansas City physicians, dentists and nurses serve at Base Hospital Unit No. 28 in Limoges, France, and establish a large "tent city" to care for more than 12,000 patients.

1918   Wheatley-Provident Hospital and Nurses' Training Association opens. John E. Perry, M.D., serves as voluntary superintendent.

1918   Eclectic Medical University, a Class-C rated medical school, closes.

1918   Central College Medical Department at 729 Troost changes its name to the Kansas City University of Physicians and Surgeons. Dr. A. L. McKenzie, president. It comes under fire in 1923 as a diploma mill, along with the Kansas City College of Medicine and Surgery.

1918   October. Influenza epidemic in the city. Dr. A.J. Gannon, city health official, orders businesses and theaters to close.

1918   City hires the first nurse nutritionist to assess school children's nutritional needs.

1919   Board of Education inaugurates a centralized plan for the education of nurses to teach hygiene, elementary nursing, drugs and solutions, and the history of nursing.

1919   Two local dental colleges merge as the Kansas City-Western Dental College.

1919   Social Services League forms as a permanent charity council to coordinate social welfare work in the city.

1920   Population of Kansas City: 324,410.

1920   City authorizes a milk-supply study, and passes the so-called North Ordinance. Health Department officials deal with the problem of an urban population that consumes 47 percent of its milk raw.

1920   Two dental college alumni associations merge to form the Kansas City-Western Dental Alumni Association.

1920   Wheatley-Provident Hospital opens a free clinic with a fully integrated consulting and courtesy medical staff.

1920   To obtain experience with children's diseases for its nursing students, Swedish Hospital affiliates with Children's Mercy Hospital.

1920   Vineyard Park Hospital opens on Hospital Hill. The 50-bed osteopathic facility performs charity work, maintaining a separate fund for this service.

1921   GH #1 opens a new outpatient facility on Hospital Hill to accommodate the growing number of patients requiring care. The Emergency Hospital and Dispensary at 6th and Walnut closes, and Health Department offices move back to City Hall.

1921   White patients complain of care from "Colored nurses" at Leeds TB Hospital. Sources cite white nurses' reluctance to serve there.

1921   City passes an ordinance to widen McCoy between 23rd and 24th to accommodate increased vehicular and ambulance traffic on the street that runs between Research Hospital and GH #1.

68

1926 First determination of viruses from bacteria.
1926 Invention of the first cathode ray tube (television).
1928 Sir Alexander Fleming discovers penicillin.
1928 Invention of the iron lung.

1921 Swedish Hospital renames itself Trinity Lutheran Hospital to avoid a public misconception that it treats only Swedish patients.
1921 Missouri passes a Nurse Practice Bill, a national model that calls for gradual increase in preliminary education.
1921 South Side Hospital and Training School for Nurses at 3007 Main changes ownership. Wildcrest Hospital Training School for Nurses affiliates with CMH to receive experiences in children's diseases. The hospital fails to receive accreditation for the 1922-23 academic year and closes.
1921 Social Services League changes its name to the Council of Social Agencies and joins with the Chamber of Commerce to sponsor Community Chest drives.
1922 First dial telephones in Kansas City.
1922 Wheatley-Provident Hospital opens a dental clinic to serve children and adults.
1922 April. GH initiates a part-pay plan in the clinic and the hospital. A controversy arises between the medical society, which opposes part-payment and the Hospital and Health Board which decides against it on the strength of the society's stand.
1923 University Hospital Training School for Nurses closes.
1923 Kansas City-Western Dental College builds a new facility.
1923 Kansas City College of Pharmacy moves to 1721-23 Baltimore, where it remains until 1943.
1923 John Edward Perry, M.D., Wheatley-Provident Hospital founder, becomes president of the National Medical Association.
1923 G. Wilse Robinson, M.D., moves

his neurological clinic to 8100 Independence Road, but the Punton Clinic at 3001 Paseo continues to operate until 1925 under separate ownership.
1924 Kansas City establishes the first urban centralized fire-alarm system in the country in a building on Hospital Hill.
1924 Public health nurses in Kansas City organize. The group includes school nurses, industrial nurses and visiting nurses.
1925 Hospital and Health Board passes a $1.2 million bond issue to build a new hospital for blacks.
1926 Christian Church Hospital closes.
1926 Wheatley-Provident Hospital receives the American Hospital Association Certificate of Standardization.

Harry S. Truman studied law after work and between terms as a county judge, an administrative post. This photo appeared in the 1924 Pandex, yearbook of the Kansas City Law School.

1926 State Board of Health revokes the charters of the Kansas City College of Medicine and Surgery at 2225 Holmes and the Kansas City University of Physicians and Surgeons at 729 Troost.
1926 Grace Hospital and Training School for Nurses closes because of controversy between nursing students and the administration.

In 1925, Mrs. Elizabeth Bruce (later Crogman), wife of Wheatley physician W. H. Bruce, founded the Florence Home for Colored Girls, a black counterpart of the nationwide Florence Crittenton homes. Mrs. Bruce convinced William Volker to fund the small, four-bedroom home for unwed mothers at 2446 Michigan, a former orphans' home. Mrs. Bruce served as volunteer director.

1926 Little Sisters of the Poor moves to a new building at 53rd and Woodland.
1926 Despite legal opposition, VA Hospital moves from its quarters at 11th and Harrison to the former Christian Church Hospital.
1926 Citizens' group attempts to found Lincoln and Lee University. The dental school affiliates with the group as the Kansas City-Western Dental College, School of Dentistry, Lincoln and Lee University.

69

Judge Henry F. McElroy, city manager and former presiding judge of Jackson County when Truman was eastern judge. In 1926, Thomas J. Pendergast picked McElroy to run the city under the new council form of government.

1926   Jabez North Jackson, M.D., prominent Kansas City physician, becomes president of the American Medical Association.

1927   WCA abandons the 21st and Tracy properties for larger facilities at 81st and Wornall.

1927   Research Hospital board honors William Volker and declares April 1 William Volker Day.

Joe Shannon, leader of the "Rabbit" faction of the Democratic machine in Kansas City and archrival of Tom Pendergast and his "Goats," had a 50-50 arrangement with Pendergast when it came to hiring at General Hospital.

Frank Niles, philanthropist and president of Niles & Moser Cigar Company, answered Dr. Katharine Berry Richardson's pleas for money to establish a new pediatric ward for black children at Wheatley-Provident Hospital. Niles and his wife later helped establish the Niles Home for Children, which still offers care at 1911 E. 23rd and 2017 E.

1927   City builds an annex to the 1911 GH #1 isolation building to accommodate chronic-care and tuberculosis patients.

1928   Jackson County Court campaigns

for and voters approve a $500,000 bond issue to construct a hospital in Little Blue, Missouri (Leeds). Harry S. Truman serves as presiding judge of the court. Construction begins the following year.

1928   Deaconess Evangelical Society opens a hospital at the former Grace Hospital location at 9th and Harrison, but loses accreditation for the training of nurses in 1932 because of financial difficulties.

1928   City begins construction of a 30-bed annex for African-American patients at the Leeds TB Hospital.

1929   City manager McElroy's Ten-Year Plan includes $2 million for municipal hospitals.

1929   American Medical University, the renamed diploma mill at 2225 Holmes, closes.

70

1925 plat map of Hospital Hill.

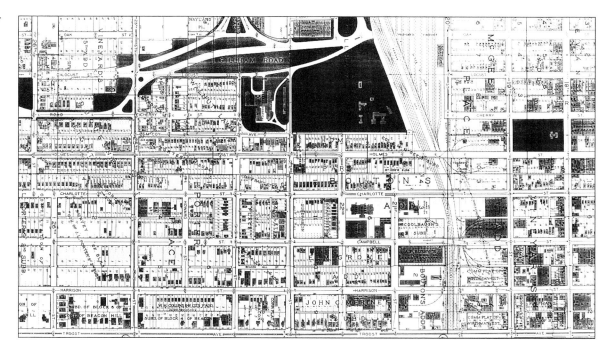

COUNT BASIE
1904-1984

In his autobiography, *Good Morning Blues*, Count Basie recalled that he was a patient at General Hospital #2 in Kansas City sometime between 1927 and 1929.

"After Oklahoma City the show moved on back to Kansas City and went back into the Lincoln Theater on Eighteenth Street. But when we finished that run at the Lincoln Theater, the Gonzelle White show was stranded again, and this time it broke up for good. But just about everybody stayed around Kansas City, which was a great town for musicians and entertainers. I don't remember what my plans were at that time, but in the meantime I got sick and had to go to the hospital.

"I forget how long I actually stayed in the hospital but it must have been for three weeks or maybe a month or more. I was not in the Phyllis Wheatley Hospital, which was right off Eighteenth Street, not far from the Yellow Front Saloon. I was in the General Hospital downtown in the area near Union Station and outside the room where I was, there was a hill that sloped right down to the window by my bed.

"That's something I will never forget, because somehow my good old road buddy, whose name was Temple and who was the drummer in the Gonzelle White show, found out that he could come that way and visit me without having to check with the nurses, and he started coming by with some barbecue and pop and other little snack goodies for me and some home brew for himself, and he would sit on the slope right outside the window, and we'd talk and have a ball. I don't know how he ever found out to come that way. I don't even know how he found out that I was in the General Hospital, unless he was the one who took me there."

Count Basie, legendary jazz musician, composer and band leader, spent time as a patient at General Hospital #2 in the 1920s.

A Children's Clinic began in 1923 and continues to the present day.

A sign on the cage admonishes patients to keep smiling.

Tom Pendergast wrote this note to "Dr. Rheinhart" [sic] with a red pen on an 8 1/2-inch by 11-inch sheet of plain paper. A contemporary of Pendergast remarked that he used "three colors of pens — black, red, and green — and if he wrote in red, you got hired."

DENTAL SCHOOL 10TH AND TROOST

Kansas City-Western Dental College building (later demolished), at the northwest corner of 10th and Troost, after the two schools merged in 1919. The building to the left housed the former Hahnemann Medical College. View: SE to NW.

In 1923, Kansas City-Western Dental College built a new facility at the northeast corner of 10th and Troost. View: SW to NE.

Roy Rinehart, D.D.S., dean of Western Dental College, called on his counterpart at the Kansas City Dental College, Charles Channing Allen, to end the rivalry that had hurt both schools since 1890. Rinehart led the two colleges after their merger.

Different drummers: a music-appreciation session for therapy and fun.

Mercy received certification from the Kansas City School District to conduct classroom education while at 414 Highland, a tradition that continued in the new building.

74

The Stadium. Nurses sometimes enjoyed afternoon tea on the playground lawn. Children often used a playhouse underneath the stone steps that served as a graduation platform, since demolished.

Mercy's chalkboard still advertised the hospital's needs — such as sheets, pillow cases, diapers, towels, home-canned fruit, jelly, pickles and relish — to potential contributors who rode streetcars or drove by on their way downtown.

CHILDREN'S MERCY HOSPITAL

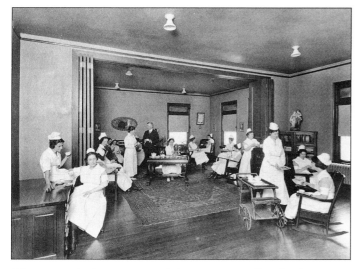

On a crisp October afternoon in 1916, Children's Mercy's Dr. Katharine Berry Richardson, along with Anna Anderson and Dr. C.B. Francisco, helped lay the cornerstone for the new hospital at 1710 Independence. The children, who were patients or former patients, represented four regions of the nation.

The audience at the cornerstone-laying ceremony even included motormen of the streetcars that would pass by the new hospital.

Mercy taught its nurses social graces as well as healing arts. Tea in the parlor became a part of the curriculum and a welcome work break.

Mercy's physicians typically wore long gowns when working in clinics.

Dr. Bob (Robert McE.) Schauffler, an orthopedic surgeon and son of Dr. Edward W. Schauffler, demonstrates a procedure in the Model Ward to an audience that included Dr. Thomas C. Unthank and Dr. John Edward Perry.

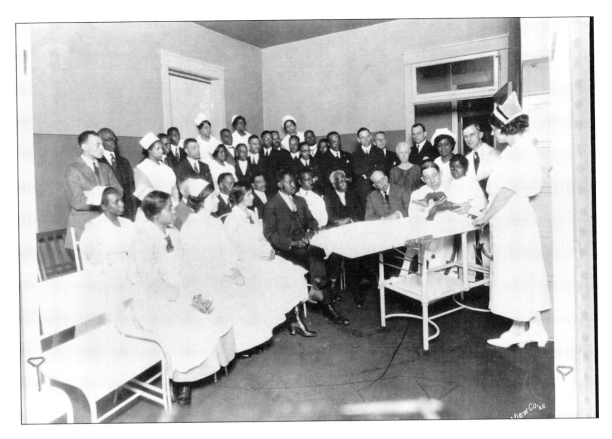

Frank Niles's check for $5,000 served as a first payment toward a new pediatric service building exclusively for black children.

Groundbreaking for a two-story pediatric addition, the Model Ward. The expansion provided 25 more beds to the eight-bed children's ward and offered more clinic space.

WHEATLEY-PROVIDENT HOSPITAL

Dr. Katharine Berry Richardson posed in front of Children's Mercy Hospital with prominent physicians she had asked to help teach Wheatley's black doctors. From left, first row: Drs. Lodge, Alvin Baer, Charles Eldredge, Homer Beal, C. B. Francisco, Sr. Second row: Drs. Lodge (a brother), Ira Lockwood, Katharine Richardson, Hugh Dwyer, John Clayton, Al Lemoine, (seated, unidentified). Third row: Drs. Curdy, Berger, Robert McE. Schauffler, H.E. Gilkey, F.C. Helwig, Sidney Pakula, Montgomery Carpenter, O.J. Dixon.

In 1924, the Urban League of America celebration at the Grand Theater honored three doctors, W.H. Maddox, H.B. Lyons and W.W. Caldwell, for receiving their certification as pediatricians under the 20-month Wheatley-Provident postgraduate program.

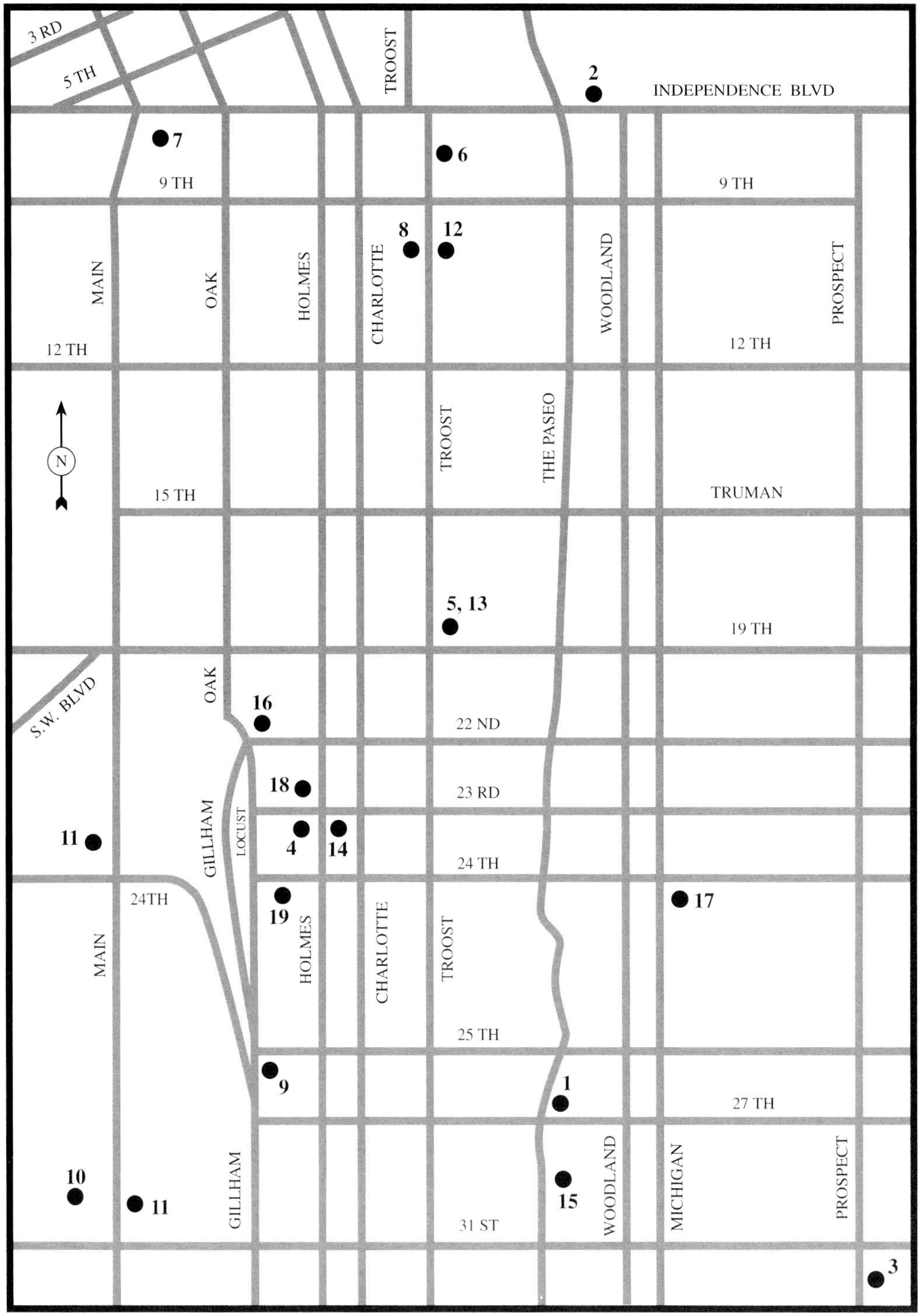

3 RD

5 TH

TROOST

INDEPENDENCE BLVD

2

7

6

9 TH

9 TH

8   12

MAIN

OAK

HOLMES

CHARLOTTE

WOODLAND

PROSPECT

12 TH

12 TH

N

TROOST

THE PASEO

15 TH

TRUMAN

5, 13

19 TH

S.W. BLVD

OAK

16

22 ND

GILLHAM

LOCUST

18

23 RD

11

4   14

24 TH

24TH

19

HOLMES

CHARLOTTE

TROOST

17

MAIN

25 TH

9

1

27 TH

GILLHAM

WOODLAND

MICHIGAN

PROSPECT

10   11

15

31 ST

3

MAP KEY

1	1916	Christian Church Hospital, NE corner, 27th and The Paseo.
2	1917	Children's Mercy Hospital, 1710 Independence Boulevard.
3	1917	St. Joseph's Hospital, Linwood and Prospect.
4	1917	German Hospital: Bardon, South Wing and Laboratory, W side of Holmes between 23rd and 24th.
5	1918	Wheatley-Provident Hospital, 1826 Forest Avenue.
6	1918	Kansas City University of Physicians and Surgeons, 729 Troost.
7	1919	Emergency Hospital, fifth floor, WalSix Building, corner of 6th and Walnut.
8	1919	Kansas City-Western Dental College, NW corner, 10th and Troost.
9	1920	Vineyard Park Hospital, SE corner, 25th and Gillham.
10	1920	Swedish Hospital Nurses' Residence, W side of Baltimore at 30th.
11	1921	Wildcrest Hospital Training School for Nurses, 3007 Main.
12	1923	Kansas City-Western Dental College, 1108 E. 10th, NE corner, 10th and Troost.
13	1923	Wheatley-Provident Model Ward, 1826 Forest.
14	1924	William Volker Diagnostic Clinic, E side of Holmes, between 23rd and 24th.
15	1924	Lakeside Hospital, 29th and Flora.
16	1925	Fire Alarm Exchange Building, 500 East 22nd.
17	1925	Florence Home For Colored Girls, 2446 Michigan.
1	1926	Veteran's Administration Hospital, 27th and Paseo.
18	1927	Research Hospital Nurses' Residence, 2220 Holmes.
19	1929	KCGH Nurse Training School and Residence, SW corner, 24th and McCoy.

Fairmount Maternity Hospital opened in 1909 at 2024 Montgall and attempted to move to 27th Street in 1915. However, neighborhood groups complained that crying babies would destroy property values. Eight years later, the hospital apparently overcame the objections and moved to 4911 E. 27th. By 1934, the hospital had moved again to the former Christian Church Hospital nurses' residence. View: SW to NE.

The Jewish community of Kansas City contributed virtually all the $1.25 million for Menorah Hospital. From its inception, Menorah served primarily as a nonsectarian institution. View: S to N.

CHAPTER SIX

A GREAT DEPRESSION, POLITICS AS USUAL AND ANOTHER WORLD WAR

When General Hospital #2 opened in 1930, the local black newspaper, The Kansas City Call, *hailed it as the "most modern public hospital in the country now ready for occupancy." View: S to N.*

When the stock market crashed on October 29, 1929, and U.S. investors lost an estimated $50 billion, most of the nation plunged into a stifling decade of hardship and pessimism. Kansas City, however, weathered the Great Depression with the most ambitious building program in its history. In the fall of 1928, Mayor Albert Beach and City Manager Henry F. McElroy had appointed a committee of 100 to study public improvement. This was to become the foundation of the Civic Improvement Committee of 1,000 that devised Kansas City's Ten-Year Plan for Public Improvement. The plan by the Committee of 1,000, a select group of civic leaders, asked voters to approve bonds for a massive city-county effort that included building a new city hall, a new county courthouse in Kansas City, a municipal auditorium, new trafficways and boulevards, several hundred miles of county roads and a new county hospital.

Boss Thomas J. Pendergast still ruled local politics through his Democratic machine. Pendergast's organization gave its endorsement to the plan, but so did many in the city and county. And even though the plan may have included a plentiful number of projects that required Pendergast's Ready-Mixed Concrete, it also contained $2 million for public hospitals.

The proposal called for renovation of the south wing of General Hospital #1 to add 100 more beds; a new, six-floor north wing with 150 beds and a new outpatient department; more operating rooms to replace the obsolete amphitheater; a new 200-bed isolation hospital and a new nurses' residence for General Hospital #2; a remodeled laundry, a new incinerator, ice and power plant; a new 60-bed third floor and another wing for white adults at the Leeds Tuberculosis unit, which the American Public Health Association had severely criticized in a recent report.

81

As part of the Ten-Year Plan For Kansas City, improvements in the municipal hospital system included the new Receiving Ward at General Hospital #1 that linked the isolation buildings with the main hospital. The unit contained a set of emergency rooms, a direct ambulance entry, an elevator for patient transfer, and an auditorium on the third floor for meetings of the Jackson County Medical Society. View: W to E.

On May 26, 1931, voters passed the Ten-Year Bond Plan by a formidable majority. Jackson County Presiding Judge Harry S. Truman, who had won election in 1926 with support from Pendergast, announced soon after the bond election he would continue county road construction. Truman had already completed many miles of new roads county voters had approved in 1928, and had overseen construction of a new County Hospital with little or no Pendergast Ready-Mixed. According to historians, Truman believed in patronage but he didn't approve of graft.

The Depression also included work on the William Rockhill Nelson Gallery of Art and Mary McAfee Atkins Museum, the new University of Kansas City and several downtown buildings that redefined the city skyline. All these projects provided jobs and opportunities for Kansas Citians in a time of crisis, but a lot of the money found its way back into the pockets of the machine bosses.

General Hospital #2 emerged as the first significant new Kansas City hospital of the 1930s. Because opposition from white residents had forced the project back to Hospital Hill instead of its desired location farther east in the black community, the city decided to build the seven-story main building next to the site of the original city hospital. The Hospital and Health Board renovated the two old brick buildings for a nurses' residence and an isolation unit for contagious patients until completion of the new building. Eventually, the board planned to replace the brick buildings with two wings on the new hospital. The board burned the remaining 1875 wooden isolation structure as trash.

General Hospital #2 represented the first new building that blacks had occupied entirely on their own, and black citizens took pride in the institution's primary mission to care for members of their race. They soon learned, however, of serious deficiencies when the Chamber of Commerce published the *Kansas City Health and Hospital Survey*, a survey of the entire municipal hospital system. The report cited several problems at General Hospital #2:

"Provisions for a morgue were made on this (ground) floor but neither natural or artificial ventilation was possible. Another morgue is under construction in the basement of the adjoining (renovated nurses') building (that) makes it necessary to transport the

Completion of the Nurses' Residence and Training School opened up General Hospital's southwest wing to renovation for patient wards. View: NE to SW.

The last Douglass Hospital, a former college dormitory at 3700 N. 27th, Kansas City, Kansas, opened in 1945 and closed in 1976. Douglass first opened in 1898 at 312 Washington Boulevard, a renovated residence in Kansas City, Kansas, then moved in 1924 to a 25-bed unit at 336 Quindaro.

Patients dine in the whites-only section of Leeds Tuberculosis Hospital in the mid-1930s.

Formerly the Nurses' Residence, General Hospital #1 remodeled this floor of the southwest wing into a women's surgical ward after nurses moved into a new residence across the street.

The city's Ten-Year Plan included funds for this ambulance building, next to the power plant and laundry. The WPA-style structure and sign remain today.

bodies of deceased patients across the lawn, down a flight of steps. In the absence of forced ventilation it is probable that unpleasant odors arising during post-mortem examinations will penetrate into the nurses' living quarters.

"Quarters for the psychopathic patients are utterly inadequate. (T)he rooms are dark and gloomy; radiators and steam risers are entirely unprotected. Toilet fixtures are present in each room and originally were screened by metal partitions. Most of these have been torn out by violent patients and the toilet fixtures themselves have been damaged.

"Throughout the building there are many evidences that the hospital was not planned by one familiar with the administration of a hospital: . . . no provision for suitable storage for X-ray films . . . no system of emergency lighting . . . drab colors used throughout the building . . . general untidiness and lack of good housekeeping . . . marked overcrowding . . . departments of the hospital are not well organized . . . superintendent of the hospital appointed in 1928 was dismissed and another put in his place . . . (i)t is commonly believed that the change was not made for the purpose of improving the service . . . employees take up their problems directly with the Director of Health instead of the superintendent . . . ."

Several years later, Dr. E. A. Walker, president of the Kansas City Medical Society, noted in his inaugural address that over the past 20 years the community had provided two hospitals with buildings and equipment totaling one-half million dollars for the training of black professionals, yet too few physicians from the black community had attained eminence in medical specialties other than surgery or nose and throat. Walker offered a remedy: "We must return to our former teachers, able teachers, who were unbiased and impartial. We need teachers of teaching ability, demonstrators who will demonstrate, superintendents who will superintend."

On Labor Day 1931, Menorah Hospital opened on Rockhill Road south and east of the Nelson Gallery, as a gift to the community from its Jewish residents. Menorah developed from a tradition of charitable medical care that dated to 1906 when Jewish doctors cared for charity patients in a storefront at 9th and Independence. Three years later, the United Jewish Social Services founded the Alfred Benjamin Dispensary

A photographer superimposed a 1934 group picture of nurses and interns over a photograph of Hospital Hill to obtain this dramatic effect. The superintendent at the time, J. H. Jennett, M.D., received his job after a car ride with Harry Truman to Tom Pendergast's office.

Harrison 8060! Everyone in town knew the number to call in a medical emergency. A General Hospital intern poses beside a Kansas City Health Department ambulance.

No historical information for this photograph exists in the General Hospital archives. Perhaps it requires only a few words. Polio. Iron lung. Child. Caregiver.

86

General Hospital participated in the Cadet Nurse Corps Training Program from 1943 to 1945.

at Admiral and Harrison to provide more comprehensive care. By 1927, prominent business and professional people had instituted a fund drive that led to completion of Menorah's $1.25 million, 130-bed facility.

Meanwhile, the idea of a city university still simmered in the minds of educators and civic-minded citizens. Although many deemed an institution of higher education a pressing need to move the community forward, the concept of a sectarian Lincoln and Lee University ran counter to some. In particular, William Volker viewed the location at 75th and State Line, the farm the Hewitts had envisioned as their gift to higher education, as far removed from the urban setting he desired. When the Lincoln and Lee drive faltered, Volker acted. As a trustee of the William Rockhill Nelson estate, he had persuaded other leaders of the university movement that the Rockhill district where Nelson had owned land afforded a more convenient locale. With that support he convinced the two other Nelson trustees to sell him 50 acres for $100,000; he then offered the land as a gift for a new university. In December 1930, Lincoln and Lee merged with the new University of Kansas City. Trustees of the two groups combined all assets, which later included Mrs. Hewitt's free title to the State Line property.

Opposition to the Pendergast machine occurred infrequently, but when City Manager McElroy installed Dr. Jabez N. Jackson, former AMA president and a prominent local physician, as the new city health director in 1933 with orders to draw up a new medical staff constitution for General Hospital, members of the Jackson County Medical Society revolted. The new constitution would deny the Medical Society the right to decide on staff privileges at General. Now McElroy and Jackson — part of the Pendergast machine — would appoint physicians to the staff. In time, Medical Society pressures forced McElroy to relent. Jackson soon died, and in 1935 Dr. Edwin H. Schorer became health director. McElroy mollified the Medical Society somewhat when he allowed Schorer once again to allow society members to offer staff privileges at the hospital. They did not receive pay, but volunteered their services.

On April 7, 1939, the U.S. government indicted Tom Pendergast on charges of income tax evasion. He pleaded guilty and on May 22 was sentenced to the federal penitentiary at Leavenworth. When auditors reviewed city funds, they found almost $20 million missing. Henry McElroy left office after Pendergast's indictment. He died that September. Pendergast returned home from prison in 1940 in poor health and died in January 1945.

With World War II in progress, Kansas City still lacked a medical school and, like most cities in wartime, experienced a shortage of doctors to care for the indigent. In 1943, the state medical society approved a resolution that urged University of Missouri officials to "exercise their abilities and energies to secure from the present State Legislature reasonable appropriations for the immediate establishment of the last two years of (clinical) instruction in medicine in Kansas City." Two years later, the university completed a survey of medical education to determine whether to expand the two-year program in Columbia to a full four years. The report stated that, in spite of the war and the resulting scarcity of doctors, their lack of abundance came from "... the uneven distribution of doctors between city and country." The survey also cited inadequate facilities for modern medical practice. Once more an effort to secure a Missouri-based medical school training program in Kansas City had failed.

Dean Roy Rinehart (in civilian suit in center) poses with the 1945 V-12 unit of the School of Dentistry.

By the end of World War II, Wheatley-Provident Hospital remained as the only private African-American Hospital in the city. The 1923 two-story pediatric annex formed the right section of the building. View: NE to SW.

1930	Great Depression begins in the U.S.	1935	Introduction of lobotomy in psychosurgery.	*leading to wide use of sulfa drugs to treat infectious diseases.*
1931	Invention of the electronic microscope.	1935	U.S. enacts the Social Security Act.	
1931	Dr. R.E. Shope isolates influenza virus.	1936	Investigators confirm the therapeutic value of sulfanilamide,	

1935 Introduction of lobotomy in psychosurgery.

1935 U.S. enacts the Social Security Act.

1936 Investigators confirm the therapeutic value of sulfanilamide,

1938 Introduction of electroshock treatment in mental healthcare.

1938 Comprehensive new federal Food and Drug Act.

1930-1945

1930 Population of Kansas City: 399,746.

1930 Many municipal hospital employees become political appointees and some return portions of their pay to the Pendergast machine.

1930 March. The newly constructed GH #2 opens. Frederick Gunn, architect.

1930 City adds a third structure to the GH #1 isolation building for male chronic patients and tuberculosis patients of both sexes.

1930 St. Joseph's School of Nursing affiliates with the College of St. Teresa.

1930 Florence Home for Colored Girls moves to a new location on Hospital Hill at 2228 Campbell. William Volker gives $10,000 to equip the four-story, brick 30-bed home.

L.P. (Perry) Cookingham, city manager after the overthrow of the Pendergast machine, helped clean up city government.

1930 Jackson County finishes its new facility at Little Blue. Although the 1928 bond issue called for construction of a hospital, the new building serves as an annex to the Jackson County Home for the next several years.

1930 Kansas City TB Society establishes a TB Clearing Center; the VNA staffs the chest clinic and follows up on patients at home.

1931 Kansas City Chamber of Commerce publishes the *Kansas City Health and Hospital Survey*, a report critical of most phases of hospital operation. As a result, General Hospital #1 renovates the south wing, formerly the Nurses' Residence.

1931 Voters pass Kansas City Ten-Year Bond Program that includes $2 million for renovation and new hospital buildings.

1931 University of Missouri curators attempt to re-establish a four-year medical school in Columbia.

1932 William Volker establishes a charitable foundation for care of the "sick, aged, helpless, distressed in mind, body or estate."

1933 Dr. Katharine Berry Richardson, the "lady of Mercy," dies.

1933 William Volker donates land that he acquires from the William Rockhill Nelson estate, as well as the William S. Dickey mansion, to help establish the new University of Kansas City.

1933 After just four years of service, the Veterans Hospital at 27th and The Paseo closes.

William Volker, Kansas City's most generous supporter of healthcare and public welfare in the first half of the century.

1935 Health Department initiates a specialized public health nursing program. Nurses work on a 12-month basis, at schools and as summer relief at GH.

1935 During the height of the Depression, GH's free clinics give medical attention to 77,572 patients, one-fifth of the population of the city. City officials turn away non-resident patients.

1936 City completes construction of the GH #1 receiving-ward building. Cost: $70,000.

1936 Voter fraud occurs in the city election. Pendergast's political machine comes under intense public scrutiny.

1937 December. Jackson County Emergency Hospital opens as a 25-bed unit for the care of indigent county patients and emergency cases, particularly county highway accident victims.

1938 First trolley bus in Kansas City.

1938 GH begins a cancer service each Tuesday at noon.

1939 *World War II begins in Europe.*
1941 *Japan attacks Pearl Harbor. U.S. enters World War II.*
1943 *Food rationing in the U.S.*
1944 *President Franklin D. Roosevelt signs the Servicemen's*

1945 *Readjustment Act (GI Bill). Harry S. Truman becomes 33rd U.S. President.*

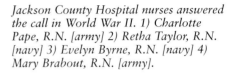

1938 Blue Cross-Blue Shield incor-porates to offer a voluntary, group prepaid healthcare plan. Subscribers and dependents pay $1 per day for any hospital stay.

1939 GH #1 and Research Hospital nursing departments affiliate with the University of Kansas City to offer three-year diploma and five-year degree programs.

1939 AMA withdraws GH #2 from accredited training of residents; interns necessarily perform the work of residents.

1939 Pharmacy school reorganizes as the Kansas City College of Pharmacy and Natural Science.

1939 Citizens form the United Campaign Committee to wrest control of the city government from the Pendergast machine.

1939 Health Department assumes responsibility for staff services at the Tuberculosis Clearing Center.

1940 Population of Kansas City: 399,178.

1940 Kansas City inaugurates a non-partisan merit system with the successful ouster of the Pendergast regime.

1940 Health Department opens its first adult health clinic at 2300 McCoy.

1940 College of St. Teresa becomes a four-year institution.

1941 Kansas City-Western Dental College formally affiliates with the University of Kansas City.

1941 GH #2 internship program receives accreditation for the training of interns.

1941 A tornado strikes Kansas City's East Side. Health Department officials set up a typhoid immunization sta-

Jackson County Hospital nurses answered the call in World War II. 1) Charlotte Pape, R.N. [army] 2) Retha Taylor, R.N. [navy] 3) Evelyn Byrne, R.N. [navy] 4) Mary Brabout, R.N. [army].

tion in the Dunbar School.

1942 GH #1 rehabilitates wards on all floors of the north side, and adds a three-story southeast wing as a part of the city's Ten-Year plan.

1942 William Volker gives $1 million to UKC.

1942 *AMA Journal* study reports the total number of black physicians has decreased five percent while the black population has increased eight percent.

1943 Kansas City College of Pharmacy affiliates with the University of Kansas City.

1945 University of Missouri completes a survey to determine whether to expand the present two-year program to a full four years.

The nurses' lounge.

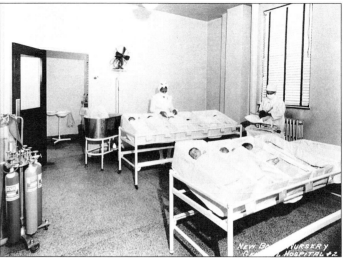

Newborn nursery, on the fifth floor.

The city's 1931 Ten-Year Plan included a new nurses' residence for General Hospital #2, and the full 10 years passed before the city began construction of the wing and a second wing for isolation of contagious patients.

GENERAL HOSPITAL #2

Kansas City physicians on the front steps of the new
General Hospital #2. Under a photo of the new hospital in
February 28, 1930, The Kansas City Call *wrote:* "The only
City Hospital in the U.S.A. ministering exclusively to col-
ored people and completely officered by a colored staff ...."
The staff included 30 physicians and six dentists.

Nursing staff of General Hospital #2, 1930.

Active medical
staff of General
Hospital #2,
1932.

In 1931, *in anticipation of the establishment of the University of Kansas City, William Volker bought the former residence of millionaire clay pipeline manufacturer Walter S. Dickey. View: N to S.*

The library. In the early years, the university used every nook in the handsome mansion for classrooms. The carriage house served as the gymnasium, and the greenhouse became the Basic Sciences building.

92

On June 28, 1945, President Harry S. Truman received an honorary Doctor of Laws degree from the university and delivered the commencement address from the south portico of Dickey mansion.

University Of Kansas City

Walt Disney designed the university mascot, the Kangaroo, years after he left town. It was in Kansas City that a friendly mouse crawling across his typewriter inspired Disney to create the most famous cartoon character in the world.

The 1933 dedication at the back of the Dickey house. It is now part of the UMKC quadrangle. View: N to S.

Walt Disney worked on property once owned by the Rev. James Porter at two locations, as an artist in 1920 for the Kansas City Film Ad company at 2449 Charlotte on Hospital Hill, and later when he opened his own studio at 1127 E. 31st.

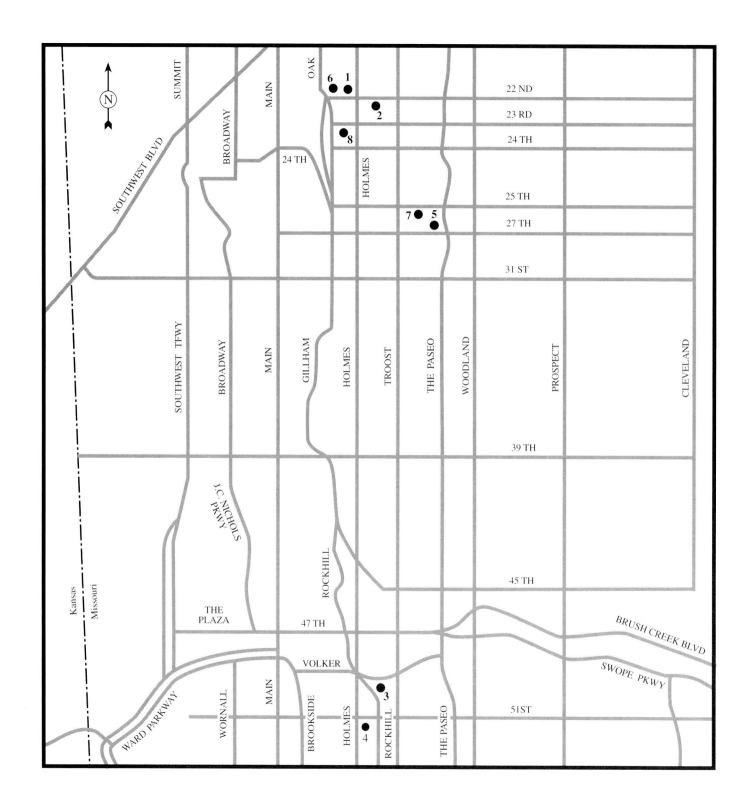

MAP KEY

1	1930	General Hospital #2, 600 East 22nd Street.
2	1930	Florence Home for Colored Girls, 2228 Campbell.
3	1931	Menorah Hospital, 49th and Rockhill Road.
4	1933	University of Kansas City, 51st and Rockhill.
5	1934	Fairmount Maternity Hospital, 1414 East 27th.
6	1935	General Hospital steam plant, 521 East 21st; laundry, 512 East 22nd.
7	1935	Robinson Neurological Hospital, formerly the Punton Clinic, 2625 Paseo.
8	1936	KCGH Receiving Ward building, 23rd to 24th and Cherry.

Postwar city skyline from the roof of the nurses' residence at General Hospital.

Troost Car #705, one of the original fleet of 24 streamlined streetcars the city placed in service in 1941.

Kansas City black servicemen. When Harry S. Truman became President, he initiated a chain of civil rights and desegregation measures.

The Isis Theater, at the southwest corner of 31st and Troost, occupied the first floor of the Wirthman Building, a favorite office location for southside professionals. View: NE to SW.

The Jones Store Co. opening at the northwest corner of 31st and Troost. View: SE to NW.

CHAPTER SEVEN

THE YEARS OF CONSCIENCE

As World War II ended, Kansas City coped with two serious problems, the dismal state of mental healthcare for indigents and entrenched racial segregation in its public hospitals. In 1946, a National Urban League report on General Hospital #2 found "heads of services (18) are not certified specialists . . . except in the case of certain white physicians. The majority of physicians in senior positions have not had training or specialized practice . . . for such positions in a major institution. Principal deterrents to the development of specialists have been the belief that the Negro community was too poor to support them and the fear on the part of the men who would like to specialize that they would not be referred enough work. Indefinite perpetuation of the racial separation plan appears to be the entrenched common denominator in the approaches of both Negroes and whites to health problems in Kansas City."

97

Carl Peterson, M.D., a postwar intern at General Hospital #2, later a general surgeon and the first black president of the Jackson County Medical Society, recalled that several young interns expressed their dissatisfaction with the hospital.

"We complained vehemently," Peterson said, "as much as we could, about the inadequacies of equipment and the fact that our mentors were not sufficiently trained to provide us with the training which we desired. The official response was that the facilities were adequate. So we complained and we complained."

When the city offered no remedies to the staff doctors' complaints, several of them organized a protest against what they termed a "lack of sufficient and appropriate medical equipment and supplies, a shortage of hospital staff and poor administration." They declared they would reduce their services until the city corrected the conditions.

"We did not threaten," Peterson said. "We did not go out on strike but we told them we would do no elective surgery."

By 1954, *the city had contracted with the Greater Kansas City Mental Health Foundation to provide professional staff for the Psychiatric Receiving Center — psychiatrists, psychologists, social workers, occupational therapists and psychiatric nurses — the first private-public partnership on Hospital Hill. Part of the professional staff included from left, front: Jurgen Thomas; Milton Kirkpatrick, M.D., foundation executive director; Marjorie Osborne, M.D. From left, back: Robijn K. Hornstra, M.D., resident; John O'Hearne, M.D., associate director; Carlos Simprini, M.D.; Don Harr M.D.*

Architectural rendering of a new General Hospital building to accommodate city hospital consolidation.

The protest proved effective, and the city implemented changes. Ultimately, General Hospital #2 acquired AMA approval for teaching interns and residency-specialty training in radiology, obstetrics-gynecology and general surgery.

Kansas City's other postwar concern, care for indigent psychiatric patients, prompted city officials in 1947 to submit a bond issue to voters to construct new wings at both General Hospitals. Before then, patients suffered from deplorable, overcrowded conditions. The bond issue passed but delays in construction created even harsher environments for patients.

In 1949, a newcomer to Kansas City became the linchpin between the concerned community and a city government that had tired of pouring tax dollars into obsolete and inefficient healthcare institutions. As a vice president of the New School for Social Research of New York City, Homer Wadsworth and his work with foundations had come to the attention of Arthur Mag, a prominent Kansas City attorney. Mag's firm handled several large philanthropic trusts in town, including the funds of the Loose family, early and prominent settlers in Jackson County. Mag convinced Wadsworth that his full-time help and advice would benefit the community in using its charitable-trust money well and hired him as executive director of the newly formed Kansas City Association of Trusts and Foundations (KCATF).

Charles Curran, former president of the KCATF, described Wadsworth: "At the time of the commotion about the 'snake pit' treatment of the mentally ill, Homer was putting together four independent trusts and he wanted to give the association an agenda."

Wadsworth's agenda proved to be the formation in 1949 of Community Studies, Inc., a nonprofit organization that would study community needs and seek solutions to them. Community Studies, Inc. laid the groundwork for creation of the Greater Kansas City Mental Health Foundation, an independent organization of psychiatric professionals that eventually provided mental healthcare services for the city's indigent under a contract with the city. Wadsworth would use the same formula a decade later to solve another healthcare dilemma.

In 1950, Kansas Citians approved a bond issue for a single building, the Psychiatric Receiving Center (PRC), rather than separate wings for both hospitals. The Mental Health Foundation began to recruit staff for the new PRC.

A devastating flood on July 13, 1951 crippled the industrial district, damaged the city water service and forced citizens in many areas to boil water. The Health Department administered 111,711 vaccinations to prevent typhoid fever.

99

Krestwoods Medical Hospital, ca. 1956, a renovated home at 2700 Tracy that sat directly across the street from where the Rev. James Porter's barn once stood. The building presently serves as a retirement home.

Dr. John O'Hearne, associate director, led this Mental Health Foundation conference. From left, Lorraine Nelson, Helen Doyle, Jurgen Thomas, Dora Karger, Marjorie Osborne, O'Hearne, Adeline Marshall, Etta Lou Wilkinson, Betty Ritchie Hornstra.

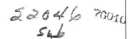

COMMITTEE SUBSTITUTE FOR RESOLUTION #22046

REQUIRING THE CONSOLIDATION OF GENERAL HOSPITALS NO. 1 AND NO. 2, EFFECTIVE IMMEDIATELY UPON ADOPTION OF THIS RESOLUTION.

WHEREAS, much study has been devoted to the necessity of consolidating General Hospitals No. 1 and No. 2, and it is the concensus of the Council that such consolidation is necessary in the interest of efficiency and economy in operation of public hospital services, and that no further delay should be permitted in accomplishing such consolidation, NOW, THEREFORE,

BE IT RESOLVED BY THE COUNCIL OF KANSAS CITY:

That the consolidation of General Hospitals No. 1 and No. 2 shall begin immediately upon the adoption of this resolution under the personal supervision of the City Manager, and shall be carried out within the following policy limitations:

1. The Council desires that the consolidation be carried out just as quickly as possible within the limits of tax dollars, personnel, staff, and necessary construction. In any event, the target date for 100% consolidation shall be May 1, 1958.

2. Such departments as may be now consolidated in the opinion of the City Manager, without injury to the present level and quality of medical services, shall be consolidated at once.

3. In the departments requiring re-alignment of physical facilities, additional construction, and/or new equipment, the City Manager shall advise the City Council, within thirty days, of his recommendations as to how much of such improvement should be made and the source of funds with which to carry out such improvements.

4. Basically, the Smith report shall be the guidepost for the orderly consolidation of the two hospitals; provided, however, that the City Manager shall advise the Special Hospital Committee every thirty days of the progress made in the consolidation, together with detailed reasons for any delay.

5. The City Manager shall call upon the executive committees of the volunteer staffs of No. 1 and No. 2 for such staffs' aid, guidance and advice in planning the consolidation.

6. The consolidation of personnel and staffs shall be made in a fair and equitable manner, using solely performance, merit, and ability as the guideposts for such consolidation. Prior education shall not be a factor since all residents and interns, being

City Resolution 22406 called for consolidation of all municipal hospitals.

100

Dr. John O'Hearne arrived in Kansas City in 1952 to work for Dr. Milton Kirkpatrick, first executive director. "I had just completed my residency at the University of Colorado," O'Hearne recalled. "We planned the construction of that hospital and we also got approval for a full three years of training by the American Board of Psychiatry and Neurology. We got that done before we moved into the new hospital in 1954."

Robijn Hornstra, M.D., presently chairman of psychiatry at the UMKC School of Medicine, recalled that when he arrived in 1954 as a new resident, the Receiving Center "was actually the first integrated facility in Kansas City. At that time there was only one restaurant downtown where blacks and whites could eat together."

In 1955, the Mental Health Foundation received accreditation for its psychiatry residency training and, in rapid succession, initiated a training program for Fellows in child psychiatry; created a Department of Research; established an After Care Clinic and a Day Hospital; cooperated with the schools of social work at the University of Missouri and the University of Kansas to give graduate students experience in the field; set up student- and graduate-training programs for nurses; and received accreditation for training programs in clinical psychology. By 1960, the foundation provided consultation services to the Rehabilitation Institute, Goodwill Industries, Ozanam Home for Boys, Spofford Receiving Center and the Family and Children's Service of Wyandotte County, Kansas.

Civil rights legislation of the 1950s and the example of a racially integrated psychiatric facility raised questions about other facets of the city's segregated healthcare system. Albert P. Mauro had come from Connecticut in 1952 as an intern in the city manager training program under City Manager L. P. Cookingham.

"We had two hospitals," Mauro recalled, "one for blacks and one for whites, and two nursing schools. Everything was separated. I was in the budget department and I found this separation difficult to comprehend."

Mauro and Curran, then a city budget officer responsible for General Hospital finances, advocated consolidation of the two hospitals.

"We were working on the health department budget together," Mauro said, "and we figured the city could save $700,000 to $800,000 a year if (it) would consolidate the two hospitals."

An early 1950s aerial view shows the University of Kansas City: the Dickey Mansion, the Geosciences building, Newcomb Hall and Haag Hall. Lower right, St. Francis Xavier Catholic Church (fish-shaped building) at 52nd and Troost; upper right, Menorah Hospital at 49th and Rockhill. View: SE to NW.

Early 1950s aerial view of Hospital Hill, before construction of the Psychiatric Receiving Center began in 1952. On the left, 1) McGee Street overpass crosses the railroad tracks where O.K. Creek ran; 2) Fire Alarm Exchange; 3) General Hospital power-plant and laundry; 4) General Hospital #2; 5) Sumner School; 6) Research Nurses' Residence; 7) former K.C. College of Medicine and Surgery; 8) Research Hospital; 9) General Hospital #1; 10) General Hospital Nurses' Training School, and to the right, private homes on Cherry and McCoy. View: W to E.

This rudimentary drawing of the proposed dentistry school at 51st and Troost appeared in a 1945 issue of The Explorer, *the alumni journal. The rendering complemented buildings on the Volker campus, where university officials expected to locate it.*

This artistic rendition of a master plan for a healthcare complex on Hospital Hill may have presented an exaggerated perspective in the early 1960s, but it did not miss the mark by far in location and configuration of some of the institutions that now make up Hospital Hill.

As the city's liaison to the Association of Trusts and Foundations, Curran worked closely with Wadsworth, whose agenda had expanded to include development of a combined city-county healthcare plan for the indigent.

"Homer thought we did not have a good mechanism for financing indigent healthcare," Curran said, "that there was too much political interference at the county level, and that General Hospital was the key for the whole community for research and training."

In 1955, Wadsworth convinced city and county officials to determine whether a combined city-county healthcare system was feasible. He again utilized the expertise of Community Studies, Inc. to examine the possibility of a Jackson County public health authority with its own board of directors and its own power to tax and issue bonds.

"There were arguments for about two years on this plan," Curran said, "but nothing happened and the report began to gather dust. But like a dog with a bone, Homer wouldn't let go."

In 1957, the economic realities of maintaining two aged, obsolete hospitals finally forced the city to consolidate General Hospital #1 and #2 and their nurses' training programs. The consolidation brought an end to segregation in all municipal healthcare facilities, but more importantly, it offered the approved training opportunities that black health professionals sought. Although General Hospital #2 never reached its full potential in the more than four decades it operated, neither in quality of training nor patient care, it did train more than 400 black physicians and several hundred nurses. And for many of them, General Hospital #2 provided the only avenue to a medical career.

Roy Rinehart, dean of the dental school at 10th and Troost, died in 1957. He had amassed a considerable amount of money from real estate that allowed him to bring his proprietary college under the aegis of the University of Kansas City, but he had not realized a further ambition, that of a dental school site in a campus setting. At that time, a nearby healthcare institution at Independence and Woodland contemplated a move from its 40-year-old facility. And in 1959, Wadsworth convinced local officials to take another look at the possibility of a combined city-county healthcare system. This time Wadsworth utilized a citizens' study committee, which he chaired, to bring more pressure to bear. The committee brought in a prominent consulting firm, Gordon A. Friesen Associates of Washington, D.C., whose recommendations included a city-county hospital district. But once more, the two jurisdictions failed to come to an agreement. Wadsworth, still intent on a solution to the indigent-care problems, kept the citizens' committee alive. It met every few weeks in the living room of Meyer Goldman, editor of *The Labor Beacon*. Events soon occurred that would bring these disparate forces together.

Margaret, Harry and Bess Truman on the rear platform of the Ferdinand Magellan *(Truman's railroad car) during the presidential whistle-stop campaign of 1948.*

Plans for the Psychiatric Receiving Center (left center), ca. 1953, included no air conditioning. City Hall contained no climate control, so efforts to include cooling equipment in the new hospital failed.

1946	First electronic digital computer.	1947	National Mental Health Act helps fund local mental health programs.	1950	U.S. Public Health Service endorses a national program for controlled water fluoridation.
1946	Hospital Construction Act (Hill-Burton) offers federal funds, primarily to help build hospitals in rural areas.	1948	President Truman initiates a civil-rights program.	1950	Korean conflict begins.
		1948	Discovery of cortisone.	1952	First hydrogen bomb explosion.

1946·1961

1946 National Urban League survey reports on problems at GH #2.

1946 City council offers use of GH #1 to the University of Missouri for clinical instruction of students during their last two years.

1947 Movement to end racial discrimination and substandard conditions at GH results in a quasi-strike. Black physicians at GH #2 attend to emergency cases only.

1946 Trinity Lutheran Hospital completes the first three floors of a new south wing.

1947 Voters approve a $600,000 bond issue for the construction of new psychiatric facilities for the city's hospitals.

1947 William Volker dies.

1947 University of Kansas City opens enrollment to all students, regardless of race or color.

1947 Community Surveys, Inc. of New York conducts an extensive study of the health, welfare and recreation

Harold Gainey, M.D. In 1947, a movement to end racial discrimination and substandard conditions at General Hospital #2 resulted in a slow-down when black physicians attended emergency cases only. The action galvanized hospital authorities to design residency training programs in several specialties and qualify #2 for AMA approval. Samuel U. Rodgers and Carl Peterson, two young black physicians, attributed the leadership of the movement to obstetrician-gynecologist Gainey.

Homer Wadsworth, executive director, Kansas City Association of Trusts and Foundations, 1949-1973.

facilities of Kansas City.

1948 William Volker Research Clinic, now the Research Clinic, moves from Hospital Hill to 107 West Linwood.

1948 College of St. Teresa offers the area's first baccalaureate degree program in nursing.

1948 GH agrees to provide communicable-disease training to Trinity Lutheran Hospital nursing students.

1949 Kansas City Association of Trusts and Foundations (KCATF) forms.

1949 Community Studies, Inc., the brainchild of Homer Wadsworth, begins operations through funding from KCATF. Dr. D.W. Bryant heads the social studies group.

1949 Polio epidemics occur in Kansas City for the following decade.

1949 Mayor William E. Kemp appoints prominent civic leaders, city officials and physicians to a citizens' committee to study mental health needs.

1950 Population of Kansas City: 456,622. The city annexes an additional 19.7 square miles.

1950 City establishes a Civil Defense ordinance.

1950 Greater Kansas City Mental Health Foundation (GKCMHF) forms.

1950 Health department inspectors insure that all milk undergoes pasteurization.

1951 Kansas City passes an ordinance to deal with general sanitation and blight in the central core. Health Department begins an education and enforcement program in 1952 that covers 600 square blocks.

1951 University of Missouri determines to place a four-year medical school in Columbia rather than in Kansas City.

1951 St. Vincent's Hospital closes its general services, but maintains an obstetrical service for unwed mothers regardless of race.

1951 Kansas City contracts with GKCMHF to administer psychiatric services in GH #1 and #2, and to assist in planning the creation of the Psychiatric Receiving Center (PRC).

1951 College of St. Teresa affiliates with GH #1 for outpatient nursing experience.

1952 City begins construction of the Psychiatric Receiving Center on 22nd Street and McCoy.

1952 VA completes construction of a 500-bed, 11-story building at 4801 Linwood Boulevard.

1952 Jackson County Medical Society builds headquarters at 3036 Gillham Road.

1952 College of St. Teresa accepts its first male nursing students in a part-time evening program.

Albert P. Mauro, former city official under L.P. Cookingham, and consultant and board member of several Hospital Hill institutions.

1952   *Polio strikes 57,628 in the U.S., mostly children.*
1953   *First description of DNA structure.*
1954   *Brown v. Board of Education. U.S. Supreme Court rejects school inte-*

gration as unconstitutional.
1955   *First polio vaccine.*
1957   *Little Rock school-integration crisis captures the nation's attention.*
1957   *Introduction of the first air-driven,*

gearless dental handpiece.
1958   *Development of the laser.*
1960   *Worldwide increase in the use of illegal psychotropic drugs.*

Charles Curran, president, Kansas City Association of Trusts and Foundations, 1973-1983.

1953   City begins serious discussions to consolidate all municipal hospitals into one facility.
1954   National Foundation for Infantile Paralysis selects Kansas City, Missouri as a site for a nationwide field trial of polio vaccine inoculations for school children. By the close of the year, the Health Department inoculates 91 percent of the school population.
1954   Kansas City Area Hospital Association (KCAHA) incorporates.
1954   Trinity Lutheran Hospital affiliates with GH's new PRC to acquire experiences for its nursing school students.
1955   Kansas City Area Hospital Association begins operation.
1955   City officials conduct an intensive study of municipal hospital funding problems at GH #1 and #2 as the aging facilities become a double liability.
1955   Queen of the World Hospital opens.
1955   Kansas City administrators consider the consolidation of all municipal health facilities. Several alternatives arise, including partial integration of GH #1.
1955   GKCMHF receives accreditation for a psychiatry residency training program.
1956   University of Missouri opens a four-

year medical school in Columbia.
1956   City appoints Dr. Herman Smith of Chicago to study the possibility of consolidating GH #1 and #2.
1956   Jackson County Court commissions Community Studies, Inc. to investigate the feasibility of a combined city-county healthcare system.
1956   GKCMHF establishes a training program for Fellows in Child Psychiatry.
1956   Hallmark expands its facility to include a portion of old Dutch Hill that rises to a peak at 25th and Gillham.
1957   A devastating tornado strikes Ruskin Heights in the southern section of the city.
1957   With consolidation of all city hospitals, GH #2 Training School for Nurses graduates its final class and merges with GH #1's nurse training program.
1957   GKCMHF creates a department of research.
1958   Nathan Stark recommends a master plan for hospital growth in Greater Kansas City through a united fund drive for hospitals.
1958   GKCMHF establishes an aftercare clinic and a day hospital for adults.
1958   Hamilton B. G. Robinson, D.D.S., becomes dean of the UKC School of

Nathan Stark, former president and board chairman of Crown Center Redevelopment Corporation, and a former senior vice president at Hallmark Cards, Inc.

Samuel U. Rodgers, M.D., executive director and founder of the Samuel U. Rodgers Community Health Center.

Dentistry.
1959   Final polio epidemic occurs. From the initial 1954 polio field trial through the end of the year, the Health Department gives more than 300,000 immunizations.
1959   GKCMHF receives accreditation of training programs in clinical psychology.
1959   Herbert Miller, M.D., a pediatrician and chairman of pediatrics at the University of Kansas Medical Center, becomes medical director of CMH.
1960   Population of Kansas City: 473,435. Metropolitan area: 1.2 million.
1960   Jackson County and Kansas City, Missouri jointly fund a healthcare feasibility study. A Citizens Study committee proposes passage of a Public Hospital District to oversee health care services for all Jackson County residents.
1960   GKCMHF initiates a major psychotherapy service.
1961   Community leaders, hospital officials and consultants formulate a master plan for improvement of hospitals in the Greater Kansas City area.

105

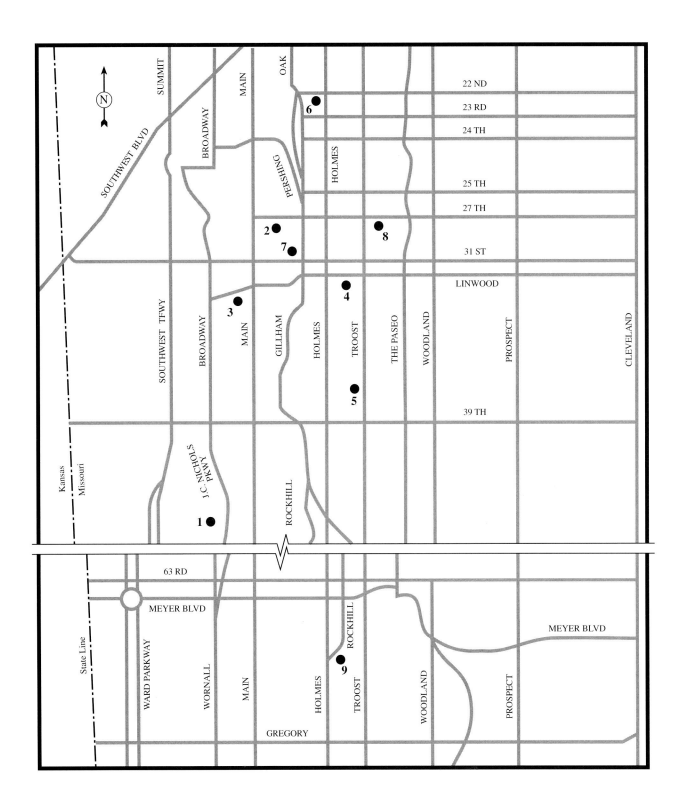

MAP KEY

1	1946	St. Luke's Hospital Annex, 4329 Wornall.
2	1947	The Rehabilitation Institute, 2700 McGee Street Trafficway.
3	1948	The Research Clinic, 107 West Linwood.
4	1949	Thornton & Minor Hospital, 911 East Linwood.
5	1950	The Rehabilitation Institute, 3600 Troost.
6	1952	Psychiatric Receiving Center (PRC), 601 East 22nd.
7	1952	Jackson County Medical Society, 3036 Gillham Road.
8	1952	Krestwoods Medical Hospital, 2700 Tracy Avenue.
9	1960	Baptist Memorial Hospital, 6601 Rockhill Road.

THE ORIGINAL INCORPORATORS
OF
KANSAS CITY GENERAL HOSPITAL AND MEDICAL CENTER — FEBRUARY 2, 1962

Left to right:
Top row: GIRARD BRYANT, LESLIE DELAPP, HUGH DWYER, ROBERT FIZZELL, JR, THOMAS GAVIN
Middle row: MEYER GOLDMAN, LEE KINSER, BERNDT KOLKER, JAMES MARSHALL, LOUIS McGEE
Bottom row: CARL MIGLIAZZO, JAMES SPELLMAN, NATHAN STARK, DALE THOMPSON, HOMER WADSWORTH

HOWARD HILL

ROBERT BATES

Incorporators of Kansas City General Hospital and Medical Center.

CHAPTER EIGHT

A NEW ERA BEGINS

After the rejection in 1960 of a city-county health authority proposal, Homer Wadsworth looked for a new approach to resolve the plight of indigents who sought healthcare from the city's deteriorating hospital system. He believed General Hospital offered the basis for a medical school in Kansas City, a long-held premise of both the hospital and the medical community. Several efforts in the 1940s to convince Jefferson City to establish a school in Kansas City had failed. In 1951, the state rejected a Kansas City offer that included free use of the entire facilities of General Hospitals #1 and #2, the tuberculosis facility at Leeds and "a spacious area south of General Hospital No. 1 as a site for a classroom and laboratory building estimated to cost 6 million dollars." To make the deal even sweeter, Research Hospital had offered to sell its "210-bed hospital, the nurses' home to the north and the power plant and laundry building to the east" for only $1.9 million. Instead, the state eventually built a four-year medical school and hospital at the University of Missouri-Columbia.

A new ally, Hallmark Cards, Inc., recently had completed an impressive new headquarters building that climbed the west face of "Dutch Hill." And another Easterner, Nathan Stark, had come to town recently and soon became Hallmark's vice-president of operations, and later president and chairman of Crown Center Redevelopment Corporation. Stark's interest in hospitals garnered him roles on the boards of Children's Mercy and Menorah and led to his work with the Kansas City Area Hospital Association and its director Sue Jenkins. These contacts and interests made him an ideal partner for Homer Wadsworth. The two of them, along with members of the city-county citizens' study committee, began to make headway with the city about the need to improve operations at the newly consolidated hospitals.

After a string of city managers came and went in a short time, Wadsworth seized the opportunity to present to the city the proposal he and the citizens' study committee and staff had drawn up along the lines of

The new Diagnostic and Treatment Center building at 23rd and Kenwood (formerly McCoy) connected with the 1942 southeast wing (not visible). The almost-completed ambulance entrance (right) sat at the north end. View: NE to SW.

The new corporate logo and name appear on the side of this ambulance.

Wadsworth's 1950 Mental Health Foundation. Under the plan, a not-for-profit group would contract with the city to operate General Hospital and the Tuberculosis Hospital (which ultimately closed). The city manager sent Wadsworth's proposal to Mayor H. Roe Bartle, who wanted relief from hospital problems. Bartle endorsed the plan and pushed it through the City Council. The corporate name of the hospital became Kansas City General Hospital and Medical Center.

Meanwhile, the county had adopted a hospital district along the lines of the two city-county studies, but without city involvement. Donald Chisholm, chairman of the new hospital board and a partner at Stinson Mag, the law firm that backed Wadsworth, also sat on the Jacob and Ella Loose Foundation boards, two of the five biggest foundations in the Kansas City Association of Trusts and Foundations — a subtle connection that would prove beneficial to Hospital Hill.

In 1962, with a new corporate board responsible to run General Hospital and with his close colleague Nathan Stark as board president, Wadsworth turned his attention to the medical school issue. The medical school at the University of Missouri-Columbia had affiliated with several institutions in Kansas City, including General Hospital and Children's Mercy, but Wadsworth believed that Hospital Hill offered much more to an autonomous school than to a satellite. Two other major institutions soon came under Wadsworth's scrutiny as possible Hospital Hill occupants and major components necessary to a medical school. Wadsworth's method to tie them together included the University of Kansas City (UKC), which had fallen on hard times.

During the late 1950s, the Association of Trusts and Foundations had funded studies to examine the relationship between the university and the community. The report that grew out of these studies observed that the university "has notable assets such as a beautiful campus, substantial buildings, well-established professional schools, and a devoted faculty." But, the report added, "to remain privately financed the University must raise $20 million of endowment." If that proved impossible, the "ultimate solution might be transformation . . . into a campus of the University of Missouri." The financial situation became so difficult that a self-study of the university, which the trusts association funded, offered lit-

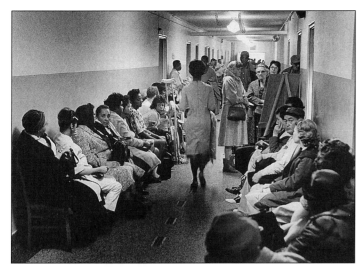

Crowded clinic hallways at General Hospital required some patients to stand and wait for an appointment. The new General Hospital and Medical Center corporation faced the problem of an aged, obsolete facility.

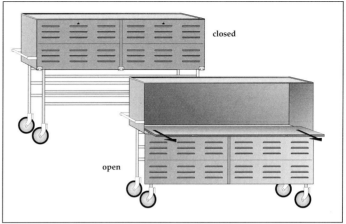

After completion of the Diagnostic and Treatment Center building, officials faced the problem of how to transport bodies of dead patients from the emergency rooms on the north end to the central morgue in the hospital basement. Hospital officials used a file-cabinet cart to move the bodies through the front lobby and crowded clinic hallways.

Architectural model of the original concept of the new city hospital and the medical school on the west side of Holmes between Children's Mercy and General Hospital. Planners agreed to build the school and the new public hospital across the street (east side) to accommodate future Children's Mercy expansion.

Upon Dr. Milton Kirkpatrick's retirement in 1958, the Mental Health Foundation named Robert H. Barnes, M.D., executive director. The next year, Charles B. Wilkinson, M.D., became director of training, and when Robijn K. Hornstra, M.D., assumed the first superintendency of the Western Missouri Mental Health Center, colleagues soon dubbed the three "The Troika."

112

Medical staff of Psychiatric Receiving Center in 1965.

tle hope for the status quo.

In *A History of the University of Kansas City*, Carlton F. Scofield, president of the UKC board of trustees and first chancellor of the University of Missouri-Kansas City, described Wadsworth in 1962 as "an aggressive advocate of the University of Kansas City being taken over by the University of Missouri."

One offer of help came from Hal Luhnow, a nephew of the late William Volker. Luhnow, who managed the Volker trust, had moved it to California. But the strings attached to the $10 million bailout included the right to name the president of the university and to purge "liberal incumbents" of the faculty.

Official transfer of all assets and liabilities occurred July 25, 1963 when the University of Kansas City officially became UMKC, the University of Missouri-Kansas City.

While the University of Kansas may have preferred Children's Mercy Hospital to be on the Kansas side of the state line, several factors contributed to the premier regional pediatric facility's reluctance to leave Missouri. Herman Sutherland, businessman, civic leader and Children's Mercy board member since 1957, recalled:

"They wanted us to move over there. We couldn't move because we had a lot of legacies that depended on the fact that we were in Missouri. We were by that time beginning to build an endowment and if we moved over there, we would have been swallowed up. The old Loretto Academy on 39th Street was for sale at that time. So we told KU that we would buy it and move our hospital there. Thank God we didn't do it. It wouldn't have been adequate. Then Homer Wadsworth was starting to work on (a medical school on Hospital Hill). So we got very excited about this and said we would like to be included. They were happy to have us."

The other institution that now envisioned a campus on Hospital Hill had planned to build on the Volker Campus. The dentistry school at 10th and Troost had become the chief financial asset of troubled UKC and had loaned the university $450,000 to pay salaries for non-dentistry faculty. When UMKC absorbed the university, Hamilton B.G. Robinson, D.D.S., Rinehart's successor as dean of the dental school, personally handed over the IOUs he had collected since 1958. Robinson had become an advocate of the Master Plan for Hospital Hill, and successfully obtained federal and

Western Missouri Mental Health Center after conversion of the former Psychiatric Receiving Center and General Hospital #2. The osteopathic University of Health Sciences Hospital and Wayne Miner public housing complex appear in the background at right.

A host of politicians traveled to Independence to observe President Lyndon B. Johnson sign the Medicare Bill at the Truman Library. Truman joined Johnson at the table. Some familiar faces on the rostrum included U.S. Sen. Stuart Symington, Missouri Governor Warren Hearnes, U.S. Sen. Mike Mansfield, Lady Bird Johnson, Vice President Hubert Humphrey, and Bess Truman.

In response to a lack of city funding support, discontented staff at General Hospital hung this hand-lettered sign over the hospital portal inscription of Portia's speech from Shakespeare's The Merchant of Venice. *One wonders if the misquoted, misspelled QUANITY (sic) purposely matched the missing T in the quotation's last word, TAKES.*

114

"... AKES." portion of speech on portal, with "T" missing.

state monies in the mid-'60s to relocate there rather than on the Volker campus.

Dr. Richardson K. Noback arrived in 1964 to help with the Master Plan. He recalled that when the major units came to some impasse on land, particularly since Children's Mercy did not want to become landlocked, and a solution appeared at hand, "Nathan Stark would use that wonderful phrase, 'I see land.' His ship was torpedoed on the North Atlantic (during WWII), and I think he was in a lifeboat with other folks for something like 31 days. Every morning the captain would get up in the bow of this little lifeboat and say, 'Land, I think I see land,' to keep morale high. That became our shorthand for smiling when something went wrong. 'I see land.' "

Another newcomer to Hospital Hill arrived about this time, not as a building but as a new entity: the Western Missouri Mental Health Center (WMMHC). In 1962, the State Division of Mental Diseases asked the Greater Kansas City Mental Health Foundation to operate jointly with them a large acute-treatment center. In the same year, the medical school at Columbia officially proclaimed the service at General Hospital's Psychiatric Receiving Ward to be a part of its training program. Kansas City voters approved the transfer of General Hospital #2 to the state of Missouri for one dollar, and the state obtained funds under the Community Mental Health Center Act to renovate it. Western Missouri, as it came to be known, opened its doors on Hospital Hill in March 1966.

But the Hospital Hill Master Plan envisioned a centerpiece, a medical school to tie the training of health professionals together with healthcare services. Wadsworth and Stark, with Mauro's help, now set out to put that final piece on Hospital Hill through a series of acquisitions that included land — 40 acres adjacent to the Hill set aside for urban renewal purposes to accommodate the new buildings — and people to join them.

One of the people who came to their support was a cardiologist, Dr. E. Grey Dimond. At 33, he had become head of the Department of Medicine at KU in 1950, and he and Wadsworth had become fast friends through their common interests in healthcare. Dimond left KU in 1960 for the Scripps Clinic in La Jolla, CA, but kept in touch with Wadsworth. On a visit Dimond made back to the

THE·QVALITY·OF·MERCY·IS·NOT·STRAINED·
·IT·DROPPETH·AS·THE·GENTLE·RAIN·FROM·HEAVEN·
·VPON·THE·PLACE·BENEATH·IT·IS·TWICE·BLESSED·
·IT·BLESSES·HIM·THAT·GIVES·AND·HIM·THAT·TAKES·

1872   1905

GENERAL HOSPITAL

With the new medical school affiliation and a change in the medicine system at the hospital, officials spruced up the old building. The repaired portal places the emphasis back on the word "takes," not "aches."

An aerial view of Jackson County Hospital and the extended-care facility before its renovation in the 1970s.

UMKC Chancellor Randall M. Whaley, School of Dentistry Dean Hamilton B. G. Robinson, University of Missouri Curator William C. Meyers Jr. and University of Missouri President John C. Weaver at groundbreaking ceremony.

The audience at the groundbreaking. View: NE to SW.

city in 1962, he first learned that Wadsworth and Stark wanted him to head a new medical school. Dimond replied, "Only if you (don't) build a four-plus-four med school. Only if you make some fun out of it." The fun became hard work as well, but the end product resulted in the six-year combined baccalaureate/doctor of medicine degree program that accepted applicants directly from high school.

Another supporter, Dr. Vernon Wilson, then dean of the medical school at the University of Missouri-Columbia and later vice-president for academic affairs, knew all three men. He had spent several years at KU Medical Center in a senior position, and he placed his considerable authority behind the Kansas City effort. UMKC Chancellor James Olson, Mayors Ilus Davis and Charles B. Wheeler, Jr., J.D., M.D., and Jackson County Executive George Lehr also played significant roles that would unite Children's Mercy Hospital, the School of Dentistry and the School of Medicine on Hospital Hill.

With the centerpiece in place, the planners next set out to bring a master's degree nursing program to the Hill. When the School of Medicine moved to its new building in 1974 and out of its three-year temporary home (the old Research Hospital Nurses' Residence), members of the nurses' planning group swiftly moved in to the building. And in November 1976 the final component of the early '60s Master Plan, Truman Medical Center, the replacement for General Hospital, sat complete atop the Hill.

Dr. E. Grey Dimond recalled the visit he and his wife, Mary, made to Bess Wallace Truman's home to ask permission to name the new public hospital for her husband: "Bess Truman was a very formal woman. I had met the Trumans in the '50s when I was at KU. Her answer was, 'Well, I don't think that will embarrass us.' "

The UMKC School of Dentistry held its dedication ceremony on March 1, 1970 in the Crown Room at Hallmark Cards, Inc. Dr. Roger Egeberg, an assistant secretary in the U.S. Department of Health, Education and Welfare, addressed the audience.

The new School of Dentistry shortly after its opening. View: SW to NE.

Children's Mercy Hospital in its new home atop Hospital Hill. View: SW to NE.

Renovated lobby of 2220 Holmes, the Research Hospital Nurses' Residence from 1929-1963, the temporary home of the UMKC School of Medicine from 1971-1974 and the present UMKC School of Nursing.

117

Dignitaries at the groundbreaking for the UMKC medical school included, from right, former mayor Ilus Davis; Homer Wadsworth, board president and executive director of KCATF; University of Missouri president C. Bryce Ratchford; Nathan Stark, a senior vice president at Hallmark Cards, Inc.; UMKC chancellor James Olson; Richardson K. Noback, founding dean of the medical school; University of Missouri curator Irvin Fane; mayor Charles B. Wheeler, Jr.; Jackson County executive George W. Lehr; Edward B. Cross, UMKC vice provost for health sciences; E. Grey Dimond, UMKC provost for health sciences and University of Missouri distinguished professor of medicine.

118

Despite the cold weather, an audience turned out for the groundbreaking at the new medical school.

In 1960, the Kansas City Area Hospital Association recommended against renovating Wheatley-Provident Hospital because of its physical condition. The Kansas City Baptist and Community Hospital Association raised funds to replace the only black hospital in town.

Martin Luther King Hospital, the replacement for Wheatley-Provident, opened May 13, 1972. The 100-bed hospital closed in October 1983 because of financial difficulties. Martin Luther King Village Apartments occupies the building today. View: NW to SE.

Aerial view of Hospital Hill, ca. 1973. The former Florence Home, with its distinctive roof gable, appears in the foreground. View: NE to SW.

A collection of hospital nursing program pins.

Ana Fernandez, staff member at the UMKC Health Sciences Library, models a vintage General Hospital cape and nurse's cap.

When Katharine Berry Richardson established the nursing program at Children's Mercy, she supposedly wrote Florence Nightingale to design the pattern for the nurse's cap.

UMKC chancellor James Olson addressed the audience at the UMKC School of Medicine dedication in 1974. Seated, from left, are medical school dean Richardson K. Noback and former mayor Ilus Davis.

The audience did not require the tent as the weather remained sunny but crisp throughout the fall day.

University of Missouri president C. Bryce Ratchford, medical student Barbara Allphin and UMKC provost for Health Sciences E. Grey Dimond, M.D., posed inside the new medical school with the ceremonial front-door key.

Federal, county, state and local officials gathered to honor the late Harry S. Truman at the groundbreaking for the hospital that would bear his name. Seated on front row, from left, Ilus Davis, Carl Migliazzo, Frank Sebree, Harry S. Jonas, Charles B. Wheeler, Jr., Edward M. Kennedy, Stuart Symington, Thomas F. Eagleton, William Phelps. The speaker was Edward J. Twin, Truman Medical Center executive director.

1963   Invention of the audio cassette.
1964   President Johnson signs the
        Tonkin Gulf Resolution.
1964   Passage of the Civil Rights Act
        prohibits discrimination in voting,
        education, employment and public

1965   facilities.
1965   President Johnson signs the
        Medicare enactment bill.
1965   Enactment of Medicaid in the
        form of block grants to states.
1965   184,300 U.S. troops enter

        Vietnam by year end.
1967   First human heart transplant.
1968   Civil Rights Act bars housing dis-
        crimination.
1970   First floppy disk.
1971   First microprocessor.

1962-1976

1962   June 1. A not-for-profit corpora-tion, the Kansas City General Hospital and Medical Center (KCGH&MC), assumes control of all GH facilities. Nathan J. Stark, president; Albert P. Mauro, interim director.

1962   September. The new KCGH&MC board names J. Frederick Sparling, M.D., director.

1962   December. CMH announces plans to relocate its 65-year-old facility to Hospital Hill.

1962   City completes a three-story Diagnostic and Treatment Center building.

1962   The Health Department Clinic moves from 2300 McCoy (now Todd Hall) to 600 E 22nd, the former General Hospital #2.

1963   January. Kansas City General Hospital & Medical Center, Children's Mercy Hospital and the curators of the University of Missouri sign an affiliation agree-ment "...in their concern for excellence in patient care, medical education and research."

1963   January. City Planning Commission declares 133 acres in the Hospital Hill area eligible for urban renewal.

1963   July 25. University of Missouri establishes a Kansas City campus, UMKC, with the merger of the former University of Kansas City.

1963   With the completion of the OB/GYN unit in the new D&TC building, all clinical services at KCGH&MC become fully consol-idated.

1963   August. After eight years of on-again, off-again construction, Research Hospital conducts dedi-cation ceremonies for its new facility at Prospect and Meyer. Harry S. Truman, guest speaker.

1963   Lakeside Osteopathic Hospital closes its 29th and Flora facility at Troost Lake. The hospital relo-cates to 8701 Troost Avenue.

1963   KCGH&MC converts the former Research Hospital for use as the Holmes Street Annex.

1963   GKCMHF receives national recog-nition as one of the eight most suc-cessful community health programs in the country. NIMH selects it as a demonstration center.

1963   Ned W. Small, M.D., becomes medical director of Children's Mercy Hospital.

1963   The College of St. Teresa changes its name to Avila College.

1964   The city formally transfers the former PRC to the administrative management of the KCGH&MC. The University of Missouri School of Medicine designates the unit as a department of psychiatry.

1964   April. A fire at Sumner School, 22nd and Charlotte, damages it beyond repair.

1964   May 12. The city presents the deed of GH #2 to the state of Missouri, and opens the way for conversion of the facility to the Western Missouri Mental Health Center (WMMHC).

1964   September. The KCGH&MC board names Richardson K. Noback, M.D., executive director.

1964   Dr. Charles B. Wheeler, Jr., becomes city coroner.

Robijn K. Hornstra, M.D., first superintendent of the Western Missouri Mental Health Center, 1964-68.

1965   UMKC completes construction of a new School of Pharmacy on the Volker Campus.

1965   Kansas City voters pass a $2 mil-lion bond issue to improve KCGH&MC buildings and equip-ment, and to acquire and clear adjacent lands.

1965   GKCMHF establishes a forensic psychiatry unit.

1965   Queen of the World Hospital clos-es because of financial problems, low white-patient usage and racial bickering among community physicians.

1965   William R. Williams becomes administrator of the Jackson County Hospital.

1965   GKCMHF opens a day-care cen-ter for disturbed children.

1965   December. Health Department clinics move from 600 E. 22nd to occupy two floors of the former Research Hospital building at 2317 Kenwood, KCGH&MC's Holmes Street Annex.

1966   The UMKC School of Dentistry (UMKC-SOD) receives federal funding for a new building on Hospital Hill; the city donates urban renewal land.

122

1972 *Introduction of the compact disk.*
1972 *December 26. Harry S. Truman dies.*
1973 *Roe v. Wade decision legalizes abortion.*
1973 *Introduction of computerized automated tomography (CAT) scanning.*
1973 *January 27. Ceasefire in Vietnam.*
1974 *President Nixon resigns.*
1975 *September. U.S. Department of Health, Education and Welfare releases new regulations to equalize opportunities for women in schools and colleges.*
1975 *Development of hepatitis B vaccine.*

1966 WMMHC and GKCMHF occupy buildings of the former KCGH #2. Robijn K. Hornstra, M.D., heads WMMHC, which assumes responsibility for psychiatric services in Kansas City and the Western Missouri region.
1966 Healthcare officials outline long-range plans for a major medical center on Hospital Hill.
1966 Jackson County Court creates a board to oversee medical operations at the county hospital, and names three physicians, one from the paid staff and one each from Menorah and Saint Luke's hospitals to provide services to the institution.
1967 June 27. A $102 million, "Catch Up-Go Ahead" county bond issue passes with more than 80 percent approval. Plans include $14 million for a new hospital teaching facility on Hospital Hill, and $2 million for the Home for the Aged at the Little Blue River.
1967 Dr. Charles B. Wheeler, Jr., wins election as Jackson County judge.
1967 A city ordinance changes the name of McCoy Street to Kenwood Avenue, from a point 425 feet north of 22nd to 24th.
1967 The Crown Center Development Corporation, a subsidiary of Hallmark Cards, announces plans to build on 85 acres of land on and around Signboard Hill.
1967 UMKC-SOD affiliates with Jackson County Hospital and establishes a 10-chair clinic at the Little Blue facility.
1968 Wayne Miner Neighborhood Health Center opens in a public housing complex at 911 Michigan. A $2.04 million federal grant provides non-discriminatory healthcare services to the economically disadvantaged. Samuel U. Rodgers, M.D., medical director.
1968 CMH groundbreaking ceremony for its new 24th and Gillham building.
1968 April. Riots in Kansas City after Martin Luther King's assassination result in widespread civic unrest. Many deaths occur. KCGH&MC staff members render emergency care to scores of victims.
1968 September. UMKC appoints E. Grey Dimond, M.D., as consultant to the chancellor for health affairs. Dimond oversees efforts to establish a new state medical school in Kansas City.
1968 County Court discontinues operation of the County Home and appoints a non-partisan, five-member hospital board to oversee operations of both the hospital and the home.
1969 UMKC submits an application to the Department of Health, Education and Welfare for construction of a School of Medicine on Hospital Hill.
1970 Population of Kansas City: 501,859. Metropolitan area: 1.39 million.
1970 March 1. UMKC-SOD dedication at its annual alumni meeting.
1970 Health Resources, Inc. (HRI) forms as a consulting and technical assistance service agency to help community health entities enhance the healthcare of Kansas City citizens.
1970 Academy of Health Professions (AHP) begins operations to establish continuing, postgraduate education programs for health professionals on Hospital Hill.
1970 May. Jackson County, KCGH&MC and Jackson County Hospital enter into a cooperative agreement to build a new teaching facility on Hospital Hill.
1970 WMMHC assumes all GKCMHF psychiatric service functions under the direction of the Missouri Department of Mental Health.
1970 June 23. Missouri Governor Warren E. Hearnes signs a $4.026 million appropriation bill for construction of the School of Medicine to match expected federal funds of $8.856 million.
1970 GKCMHF expands its psychiatric service, research and education roles, both independently and in conjunction with WMMHC.
1970 Edward J. Twin, M.D., becomes executive director of KCGH&MC and consultant to the board of directors.
1970 September 14. The charter class of 18 at UMKC-SOM begins studies.
1970 Jackson County Hospital receives accreditation to operate a resident-care division from the Joint Commission on Accreditation of Hospitals, but the state of Missouri withholds licensure because of the hospital's failure to meet certain physical requirements.
1970 December 17. CMH moves from

Independence Avenue to Hospital Hill.

1971   Dr. Charles B. Wheeler, Jr., becomes mayor of Kansas City.

1971   WMMHC builds the Regional Diagnostic Center, on the northwest corner of 22nd and Holmes, to serve mentally retarded and developmentally disabled clients.

1971   Jackson County Hospital occupies Mission East Nursing Home at 911 East Linwood while it renovates the County Home.

1971   UMKC appoints Dr. Richardson K. Noback dean of the School of Medicine.

1971   KCGH&MC restructures its general medicine department to conform with the new medical school's docent concept of patient care.

1971   KCGH&MC announces it will phase out its School of Nursing

Hamilton B. G. Robinson, D.D.S., UMKC School of Dentistry dean, 1963-1975.

because of rising operating costs, small enrollment and high dropout rate.

1971   Kansas City Southwest Clinical Society occupies new offices in the Health Sciences Building, 2220 Holmes.

1971   UMKC-SOD expands its dentistry clinic at Jackson County Hospital to 30 chairs and receives accreditation for the unit from the American Dental Association.

1971   The city adopts an ordinance to relinquish ownership of its ambu-

In 1973, UMKC health sciences officials called on Luisita Archer, R.N., a Children's Mercy employee, to help set up the curriculum for a graduate nurse program. She remained as the interim director of the program for several years.

lances, and to contract with private companies to provide emergency vehicles.

1971   Wayne Miner Neighborhood Health Center moves to a new facility at 8th and Euclid.

1972   January. UMKC-SOM groundbreaking.

1972   Hospital Hill Health Services Corporation (HHHSC) incorporates. The not-for-profit, group-practice organization provides multi-specialty medical faculty for the School of Medicine and the university's affiliated teaching hospitals.

1972   CMH initiates a graduate nurse academic and clinical training program in pediatrics.

1972   JCMS elects Carl M. Peterson, M.D., president. Dr. Peterson becomes the first black physician to head the group.

1972   Martin Luther King Memorial Hospital opens at 2525 Euclid to

Walter Ricci, M.D., superintendent at the Western Missouri Mental Health Center, 1973-1980.

replace Wheatley-Provident. King Hospital sits a block from a site the black community selected in the 1920s for GH #2.

1972   UMKC completes the Biological Sciences Building and the Spencer Chemistry Building.

1973   May 6. Jackson County Public Hospital ceremony for its $5.5 million expansion project. With a new home-rule charter government that replaces the three-judge County Court, Jackson County contractually transfers its hospital facilities to the control of the KCGH&MC corporation.

1973   Mid-America Regional Council Emergency Rescue (MARCER) establishes an ambulance service to coordinate the city's emergency transportation needs.

1973   September 8. Groundbreaking ceremony for the new Truman Medical Center facility on Hospital Hill. Federal, county, state and city representatives attend.

1973   Homer Wadsworth, executive director and president of the KCATF board, resigns to accept the presidency of The Cleveland Foundation. Charles E. Curran, KCATF vice-president, succeeds Wadsworth.

1973   UMKC develops a clinical nursing masters program.

1974   KCGH&MC issues revised payment-of-care guidelines regarding medical indigence.

1974   UMKC-SOM, the Kansas City Southwest Clinical Society and the Masters Track and Field Association sponsor the first Hospital Hill Run.

1974   UMKC initiates a doctor of pharmacy program.

1974   Nathan Stark resigns the presidency of Crown Center Redevelopment Corporation and the chairmanship of the

KCGH&MC board of directors to accept a position as vice chancellor for the health professions at the University of Pittsburgh.

1974   October 27. UMKC-SOM dedication.

1974   Some Health Department clinics move to 1423 E Linwood, a former Greek Orthodox Church.

1975   Spring. Marvin Revzin, D.D.S., becomes dean of the School of Dentistry, succeeding Dr. Hamilton B. G. Robinson.

1976   July 26. UMKC administration publicly announces the Association of American Medical Colleges' (AAMC) invoking of probationary status on the medical school program.

1976   Jerry F. Stolov becomes the first executive director of the Hospital Hill Health Services Corporation.

1976   Jackson County Hospital completes renovation of the former Home for the Aged and Infirm.

1976   Welcome House, Inc. moves to 2751 Charlotte where it operates a 36-bed facility for recovering alcoholics.

1976   November 14. TMC West dedication.

1976   November 29. Jackson County Hospital officially becomes Truman Medical Center East.

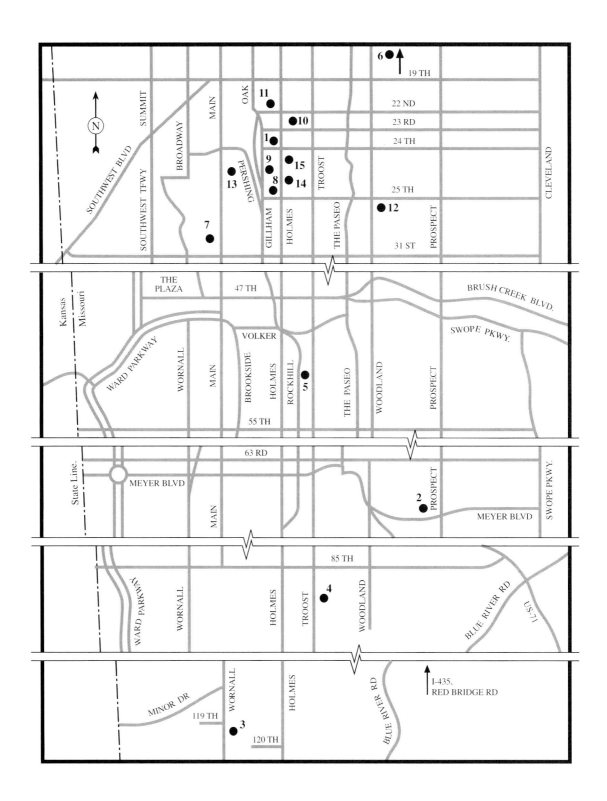

MAP KEY

1	1962	KCGH Diagnostic & Treatment Center, McCoy (Kenwood), 23rd to 24th.
2	1963	Research Hospital, 2316 East Meyer.
3	1963	Avila College, 11901 Wornall.
4	1963	Lakeside Hospital, 8701 Troost.
5	1965	UMKC School of Pharmacy, 51st and Rockhill.
6	1968	Wayne Miner Neighborhood Health Center, 911 Michigan.
7	1969	Rehabilitation Institute, 3011 Baltimore.
8	1970	UMKC School of Dentistry, 650 East 25th.
9	1970	Children's Mercy Hospital, 2401 Gillham Road.
10	1971	Brothers of Mercy Extended Care Facility, 2211 Charlotte.
11	1971	WMMHC Regional Diagnostic Center, 610 W 22nd.
12	1972	Martin Luther King Memorial Hospital, 2525 Euclid.
13	1974	Crown Center Complex, 24th and Main.
14	1974	UMKC School of Medicine, 2411 Holmes.
15	1976	Truman Medical Center, 2301 Holmes.

Truman Medical Center West dedication. View: NW to SE.

Architectural rendering of the Eye Foundation of Kansas City. View: E to W.

128

In 1988, the Ronald McDonald House opened its 100th home at 25th and Cherry. View: W to E.

CHAPTER NINE

TOPPING OFF THE HILL

oon after Truman Medical Center became a bricks-and-mortar reality, many of the visionaries who had worked to rejuvenate Hospital Hill were gone or soon moved on to accept new responsibilities and challenges.

New leaders now began to appear on Hospital Hill with the task of sustaining and improving the legacy of the visionaries. In 1975, Richard Biery became city health director and began to strengthen the Health Department.

129

"The two directors before me really had quite a challenge reconsolidating the department," Biery said. "In the old agreements the city was to give legal support to the hospital, and the hospital was to give laboratory support to the Health Department. Gradually, as the institutions grew apart, it began to dawn on us that those old working relationships didn't really exist anymore and that we needed to begin to formalize."

In 1976, Jerry Stolov became executive director of the Hospital Hill Health Services Corporation (HHHSC), a faculty practice system of physicians who provided professional services on a contractual basis to Hospital Hill institutions. HHHSC repeated the success of earlier groups, such as the Mental Health Foundation and the General Hospital corporation, by using the same formula of separating politics from healthcare. Stolov recalled his task:

"The medical school was building to 100 students per class and we had to recruit faculty to be able to keep up with the curriculum. As the school matured, and we moved into the new hospital, our clinical activity greatly increased. The corporation today includes 125 full-time attending staff doctors, 110 part-time staff doctors, 300 house-staff doctors, 23 fellows and 69 support staff. We are proud to serve all patients at Truman Medical Center West and East and other institutions served by the county and city."

The change in the corporate name of Kansas City General Hospital and Medical Center to Truman Medical Center honored a revered local citizen.

Hospital Hill Center. View: E to W.

Model of Children's Mercy capital improvement project. View: N to S.

James J. Mongan, M. D., executive director of the hospital corporation since 1981, remembered that the name change and a medical facility of the highest quality did not necessarily alter the immediate perception many in Kansas City held of healthcare for indigents.

"The first seven years I was here I might call lean years," Mongan said. "Public hospitals have traditionally been somewhat underfunded. They have a special mission to serve the indigent or low-income population. They have to go to the city and the county for the funding base to provide that indigent care. And city and county governments have not been in a position historically to give you all the dollars that you ask for. The net effect of that, both here on Hospital Hill and in other public hospitals around the country, tended to (create) somewhat fraying safety nets that encountered difficulty in maintaining quality standards. A lot of people here on the Hill have worked hard for many years to keep these institutions running at a high-quality level. They did that with some success.

"By the mid- to late-'80s, with steadily increasing numbers of indigent patients and the continued squeeze on city and county budgets, we found ourselves on the brink of bankruptcy. We were rescued by a vote of the citizens, which I think says a lot about the base of political support that had been built up through the years, and got an increase in the health levy which put us back on our feet. We were helped enormously in 1989 by some changes in the Federal Medicaid law that brought in an additional stream of financing to Hospital Hill. So from the period of roughly '88 through '95, the last seven years or so, I sure wouldn't call them seven fat years, but I would call them seven years of a relatively more sound funding base. We have used that increased funding base to try and bring our facilities up to date. Truman is in the midst of a significant renovation and catch-up in our capital needs here on Hospital Hill. Between Children's, Truman, the university and the city, there is almost $150 million worth of construction, planned and underway. We have been trying to build a strong base for the future while we are in a position to do it."

When the Eye Foundation of Kansas City opened on Hospital Hill in 1986, the design presented a new look in contrast to the brick structures that surrounded it.

Architect's rendering of the Truman Medical Center East Care Centre & Ambulatory Emergency Services Expansion/Renovation Project.

The Bert and Walter Berkowitz Helipad at Truman Medical Center, a gift of the Tension Envelope Foundation, the Tension Envelope Corp. and its employees.

When the city completed the Psychiatric Receiving Center, the Cold War had begun to escalate. This Civil Defense fallout shelter sign remains today on the side of the building. View: E to W.

Dr. Felix Sabates, president of the Eye Foundation and the man responsible for creation of the unique building, has enjoyed a 34-year relationship on Hospital Hill.

In 1962, he began to travel on a regular basis from the medical school at Columbia to supervise ophthalmology residents who rotated through General Hospital. Sabates, a native of Cuba, had studied under Dr. Charles Schepens at the renowned Eye Research Institute at Harvard. As a newcomer to this country, Sabates recalled his first impression of Hospital Hill: "Dr. John Buesseler, chairman of the department, brought me up from Columbia the first time. The eye facility was in the basement of General #1. There was no air conditioning, no equipment. These were the worst conditions of any hospital that I had seen in Cuba. The big promise was that money was coming in and that the hospital was going to get better soon."

Sabates moved to Kansas City to open a private practice in 1966, but retained a part-time appointment to oversee General's eye clinic. He also created an independently accredited residency that soon affiliated with the new UMKC School of Medicine. As a sort of stepchild department, Sabates and his staff moved from area to area through the years, but when Truman Medical Center opened he moved to the Diagnostic and Treatment Center building. He also began to experiment with lasers and eventually amassed the latest available for eye surgery.

"We created the Eye Foundation in 1986," Sabates said. "I gathered a group of eye doctors and they came to the basement of my house. Many were doubtful about what we were trying to do, so I said to them, 'Let's form a not-for-profit organization and let's call it the Eye Foundation of Kansas City, and the purpose of the foundation will be to support the eye department at the hospital and the school.' "

One of the most divisive issues Hospital Hill encountered since the late '50s and early '60s came over the proposed demolition of the 1908 General Hospital building. In 1983, both Children's Mercy Hospital and the Truman Medical Center began negotiations with the city to raze the building for expansion of Hospital Hill facilities. In 1985, the city council set up a task force to determine within 90 days possible ways to use the building. General Hospital had been a city landmark for eight decades,

After 66 years, ready for the wrecking ball. In 1977, Truman Medical Center demolished the Holmes Street Annex, formerly Research Hospital, formerly German Hospital.

On October 29, 1993, First Lady Hillary Rodham Clinton visited Truman Medical Center to participate in a round-table discussion with Hospital Hill officials. From left to right: Rev. James D. Tindall, Fong Y. Tsai, M.D., Stephen McDaniel, Rosa Miller, R.N., Hillary Rodham Clinton, E. Grey Dimond, M.D., Dianne Cleaver.

and efforts to retain the structure pitted preservationists against Hospital Hill healthcare professionals who were running out of room. The preservationist community, opposed to the hospital's destruction, objected to the short time limit.

Mayor Richard Berkley recalled: "The discussion of what to do with old General Hospital intensified (in city council meetings) in 1988. I personally was in favor of preserving it if realistic, and if not, preserving the facade so that you could view that as you drove down Gillham Road." The dispute between Hospital Hill institutions and the preservationists dragged on for years.

Berkley and his administration faced an even more critical decision on indigent healthcare.

"Truman Medical Center has always been a significant part of the city budget, next in size to that of the police department," Berkley said. "The financial strain on the city was severe. We decided to put a health levy (a half-cent sales tax) on the ballot in 1988 but it failed. I told the council I thought we ought to go back very quickly to the voters and try again because without that tax, we would have serious problems. Something else was on the ballot that first time which was distracting. The second time, we were more focused and the levy passed."

Eventually, Children's Mercy Hospital's need for expansion brought about the demolition of old General Hospital. For years a misconception persisted that the deed to General Hospital restricted the use of the property to hospital or hospital-related purposes — that Col. Thomas H. Swope's will did not allow other uses of the land. A 1985 Landmarks Commission memo to the city council, however, had clarified that no restrictions existed in the deed, so Frederick Gunn's building eventually came down. One cannot overlook a certain irony that a hospital went down for a new parking and outpatient structure, and a parking structure went down for a new hospital.

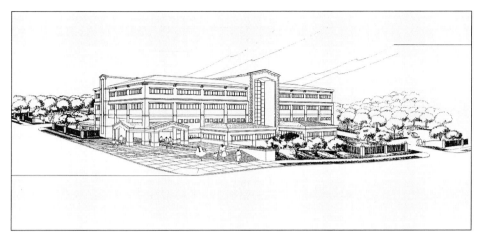

The new Kansas City Missouri Health Department building will stand where millionaires' mansions once stood on Troost Avenue.

Workers salvaged General Hospital's gargoyles and the front portal inscription during demolition. Truman Medical Center officials have preserved the portal and will install it at Truman Medical Center West.

135

1978   *First in vitro fertilization. First test-tube baby born.*

1979   *World Health Organization (WHO) announces the eradication of small-pox.*

1981   *December. Researchers identify a*

1982   *new viral disease, Acquired Immune Deficiency Syndrome (AIDS).*

1982   *First permanent artificial heart.*

1982   *Introduction of magnetic resonance imaging (MRI).*

1983   *June. National health officials*

   declare blood transfusions pose little risk as a cause of AIDS.

1984   *French and U.S. researchers identify the human immunodeficiency virus (HIV) that causes AIDS.*

1985   *French researchers announce the*

1977-1994

1977   At the request of the Missouri Department of Mental Health, GKCMHF resumes an active role in providing clinical services at WMMHC.

1977   St. Joseph's Hospital moves from Linwood and Prospect to a new 300-bed building on a large-acreage site at Interstate 435 and State Line. The hospital pioneers the use of helicopters in the Kansas City area to transport critically ill or injured patients.

1977   George A. Russell becomes chancellor of UMKC.

1977   UMKC-SOM receives notice from the LCME of full accreditation and the removal of its probationary status.

1977   September. Brush Creek flood kills 25.

1977   October. Kansas City School District requires compliance with Missouri's childhood immunizations law. Health Department workers immunize more than 12,000 school children.

1978   John Ashley, M.D., becomes executive director of TMC West.

1978   U.S. Supreme Court rules favorably for the UMKC-SOM in the Horowitz Case, brought about by the school's dismissal of a female

Nicola T. Katf, M.D., superintendent of Western Missouri Mental Health Center, 1968-1973.

Marvin Revzin, D.D.S., dean of the UMKC School of Dentistry, 1975-1982.

student for her unsatisfactory clinical performance despite her excellent scholastic performance.

1978   CMH appoints Richard L. Dreher, M.D., executive director.

1978   State of Missouri settles a claim on the William Volker Fund that provides $3 million in memorial grants to several Kansas City area civic, charitable, educational and healthcare institutions.

1978   TMC East opens a new mental health unit.

1978   Harry S. Jonas, M.D., becomes dean of the UMKC School of Medicine.

1979   Richard M. Biery, M.D., city health director, begins a reorganization of the ambulance service, setting rigorous new standards for

Richard S. Dreher, M.D., executive director of Children's Mercy Hospital, 1978-1986.

Harry S. Jonas, M.D., dean of the UMKC School of Medicine, 1978-1987.

response times and training of emergency technicians.

1980   Population of Kansas City: 448,159. Metropolitan area: 1.45 million.

1980   TMC East opens an advanced dentistry clinic.

1980   UMKC-SOM receives a $710,771 grant to establish a department of community medicine and family practice at TMC East.

1981   James J. Mongan, M.D., becomes executive director of Truman Medical Center.

1981   UMKC-SOD conducts its centennial celebration.

1981   Kathleen Bond, R.N., Ed.D., becomes dean of the UMKC School of Nursing.

1981   June 6. TMC East groundbreaking for its new family practice center.

1981   July. The Hyatt Hotel disaster kills 113. Medical students and TMC personnel on call attend to the injured and dying patients.

1981   UMKC-SON initiates a Bachelor of Science program for registered nurse graduates of associate degree or diploma programs.

1981   B. W. Sheperd State School for the Severely Handicapped moves from

1987   formulation of a drug that inhibits the AIDS virus.
1987   First meningitis (conjugate) vaccine.
1989   Supreme Court rules states may restrict access to abortions.
1990   FDA approves the time-release

1994   birth-control implant.
1994   British researchers identify the genetic cause for Lou Gehrig's disease, amyotrophic lateral sclerosis (ALS).
1994   Scientists identify the gene responsi-

1994   ble for Huntington's disease.
1994   New strains of drug-resistant bacteria occur worldwide.

Beverly F. Wilson, M.D., M.P.A., superintendent of Western Missouri Mental Health Center, 1980-1983.

1600 Linwood to a newly constructed facility at 2727 Tracy on the exact site of Rev. James J. Porter's 1834 cabin.

1982   After the retirement of Dr. Marvin Revzin, Russell Sumnicht, D.D.S., assumes the School of Dentistry deanship.

1982   TMC East completes construction of the Bess Truman Family Practice Clinic, a new emergency room and a new psychiatric rehabilitation unit.

1983   October. Martin Luther King Hospital closes because of financial problems. Newspaper accounts cite mismanagement for its failure.

1983   Health Department reports the first AIDS case in Kansas City.

1983   TMC East completes a new maxi-

Morty Lebedun, Ph.D., M.S.W., superintendent of Western Missouri Mental Health Center, 1984-1988.

mum-care unit.

1984   UMKC establishes a biological sciences school with a faculty that teaches both Arts and Sciences and medical studies.

1984   TMC East opens a new ophthalmology clinic.

1985   UMKC names Michael J. Reed, B.D.S., Ph.D., dean of the School of Dentistry.

1985   School of Dentistry establishes an outreach program to deliver care to underserved, impoverished citizens in Venezuela, especially children.

1986   The Eye Foundation of Kansas City completes its unique structure on the site of the former Research (German) Hospital at the SW corner of 23rd and Holmes.

1986   School of Dentistry undergoes a multimillion-dollar renovation to modernize its clinics. Innovations include the Orlando and Harriett Sommers Clinic for Dental Faculty Practice and Advanced Education Program.

1986   Welcome House, Inc., a not-for-profit program for recovering alcoholics, moves from a leased house at 25th and Holmes to a 73-bed working house in the old Christian Church Hospital nurses' residence.

1986   St. Joseph's Hospital changes its name to Saint Joseph Health Center.

1987   UMKC appoints James A. Mongan, M.D., dean of the School of Medicine. Mongan, executive director of Truman Medical Center, retains both titles

James J. Mongan, M.D., dean of the UMKC School of Medicine since 1987, and executive director of Truman Medical Center since 1981.

and duties.

1987   UMKC-SOD enrolls the first class of students in its six-year combined BA/DDS degree program and establishes an interdisciplinary Ph.D. program.

1989   UMKC and Saint Luke's announce an agreement for the hospital to become a primary teaching affiliate of the School of Medicine.

1989   Regional Diagnostic Center for Mentally Retarded moves from Hospital Hill to Admiral Boulevard. The 610 West 22nd building becomes the child psychiatry facility for WMMHC.

1989   UMKC-SON begins satellite telecasts of master's degree nurses' programming to students at the

137

William Craig, Ph.D., superintendent of Western Missouri Mental Health Center, 1988-1992.

university's St. Louis campus.

1990 Population of Kansas City: 434,829. Metropolitan area: 1.58 million.

1990 Completion of Longfellow Heights, Phase I, a multimillion-dollar apartment complex project on Hospital Hill.

1991 UMKC names Nancy Mills, Ph.D., interim dean of the School of Nursing; she becomes dean in 1993.

1991 E. Grey Dimond, M.D., provost emeritus for the health sciences, announces an endowed gift of his

Kathleen Bond, R.N., Ed.D., dean of the UMKC School of Nursing, 1981-1991.

138

home, Diastole, to the university for meetings and social functions. Official name for the facility: The Mary Clark and E. Grey Dimond Scholars Center.

1992 Hospital Hill Center opens.

1992 UMKC-SOD establishes the Clinical and Applied Research Center for testing and evaluating dental materials, techniques, equipment and protocols.

1993 CMH concludes a successful capital improvements fund drive, raising $52 million to expand clinic and parking facilities.

1993 Hillary Rodham Clinton, wife of President Bill Clinton, visits TMC during her nationwide tour to help formulate a national health-care program for Congressional approval.

1994 UMKC-SOD expands its annual alumni meeting to a regional scope and renames it the Midwest Dental Conference.

1994 Construction begins on the CMH

building expansion program.

1994 TMC begins construction on a parking structure on the east side of Holmes, partly on the site of the former Florence Home.

1994 TMC East initiates a $14 million renovation and expansion project of its long-term care and emergency-ambulatory facilities, due for completion in1997.

1994 The University of Missouri receives approval to establish an intercampus Ph.D. program in nursing at Kansas City, Columbia and St. Louis. Kansas City will admit the first students in the shared-campus program in 1995.

1994 GKCMHF moves off Hospital Hill for the first time since its inception.

1994 Modernization and renovation of the dental clinic at TMC East begins. The clinic offers preventive, chronic and emergency care for family members.

New Swope Parkway Health Center under construction at Blue Parkway and Cleveland Avenue. The executive director is E. Frank Ellis, son of Frank Ellis, M.D., former executive director of General Hospital #2. View: N to S.

HEALTHCARE CLINICS

Samuel U. Rodgers Neighborhood Clinic East complex. Woodland Magnet School and the former University of Health Sciences Hospital appear in the background. View: SE to NW.

The Kansas City Health Department facility at Linwood and The Paseo, one of several centers the department operates to provide healthcare services. View: NE to SW.

The Richard Cabot Clinic incorporated under that name in 1923, in honor of Dr. Cabot. St. Luke's Hospital conducted a weekly free clinic at 1843 Pennway, then at 721 W. 18th. Until recently, Children's Mercy maintained a longtime arrangement for pediatric care there. View: NE to SW.

Todd Hall, Hospital Hill. Formerly the General Hospital isolation building, the Health Department has used the facility for several years. View: NW to SE.

Dr. Felix Sabates presented Dr. Dominic Tutera a plaque for his contribution to the Eye Foundation building. Dr. Tutera, a prominent builder and head of the Tutera Group, waived his construction fee and arranged financing for the loan.

140

The Eye Foundation dedication audience paused for refreshments and then toured the new building. View: NE to SW.

EYE FOUNDATION OF KANSAS CITY

Truman chairman E. J. Holland, Jr. spoke at the foundation's groundbreaking. View: E to W.

The unique design of the Eye Foundation lends a new aspect to Hospital Hill.

Moving the first shovelful at the Eye Foundation groundbreaking, from left, Felix Sabates, M.D., president and founder; John Irvine, M.D.; E. Grey Dimond, M.D.; Dominic Tutera, M.D.; Don Chisholm; James J. Mongan, M.D.; and E. J. Holland, Jr.

The cornerstone for Children's Mercy Hospital still sits in place on the east wing of 1710 Independence, which the University of Health Sciences, an osteopathic college, now occupies. Mercy co-founder Dr. Katharine Berry Richardson documented the contents of the box with names of the women's governing board, the board of trustees, Mercy nurses at the time and the four children who participated in the laying of the cornerstone.

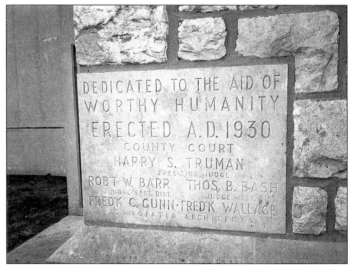

Frederick Gunn had help with the design of the 1930 Jackson County Hospital from Frederick Wallace, a brother-in-law of Harry Truman.

The main Research Hospital building denoted 1886 as its founding date although the hospital did not change names until March 1918.

W. C. Root supposedly designed the bronze tablets set in terra cotta at the west entrance of General Hospital. The other tablet read: "Because of his love for his fellow man, Thomas H. Swope gave to the people of Kansas City the site of these buildings."

CORNERSTONES

Frederick C. Gunn,
Rensselaer Polytechnic '87
Architect
1023 Grand Avenue
Kansas City, Mo.

January 17, 1906

Greeting:

This letter is penned upon the day this stone is closed.

My father the late Major Otis B. Gunn, died Feb. 18, 1901 and is buried in the family lot in Oak Hill Cemetery, Lawrence, Kansas. My mother Mary H. (Crosby) is not in good health and is almost 74 years old. My sister Mrs. Herbert W. Whitebrad lives in La Grange near Chicago. She has eight children: Helen, Laura, Otis, Vera, Margaret, Thomas and Francis. My sister Ellen (Nellie) married a musician Bendix who died two years ago, she has no children. I am 40 years old. I married Winifred Berst in 1893. We are in good health but have no children. We are now building a house of native stone at 3701 Valentine Road, Roanoke.

I am architect (sometimes associated) of the court houses at Beatrice, Nebraska., Clinton, Mo., Ft. Worth, Texas, Huntington, West Virginia, Rock Island, Illinois, Emporia and Lawrence, Kansas and of the libraries at Salina, Kansas, and Carthage, Mo., and was local superintendent of the new Post Office here for 6 1/2 years, from which position I was dismissed on trivial charges by the Republicans.

Through the partisan administration of Mayor Neff, I (a Democrat) was forced to associate with Root and Siemens in the plans for this hospital.

They have two votes to my one and some parts of this building were forced upon me over my protest for more substantial work.

I was a member of the 3rd regiment VFW for three years, a councilman 1892-1893, the Mason Temple Lodge #299, and member University Club.

God bless you and may be prosperous our country. In great haste,

Frederick C. Gunn.

The contents of the recently opened 1906 General Hospital cornerstone included annual reports of the City Water Works, a copy of the city council resolution authorizing the building, the 1903 newspaper detailing Col. Thomas H. Swope's gift of land and a handwritten letter from Frederick Gunn. In it, Gunn admits he wrote hastily, which may explain why he listed only seven of his sister's eight children.

143

Frederick Gunn, architect of three Truman Medical Center buildings: General Hospital in 1908, the isolation building (Todd Hall) in 1911 and Jackson County Hospital in 1930.

MAP KEY

1   1977   Diastole, 2501 Holmes.
2   1984   Berkowitz Helicopter Pad, E side Charlotte at 24th.
3   1986   Eye Foundation of Kansas City, 2300 Holmes.
4   1988   Ronald McDonald House, 2501 Cherry.

5   1990   Longfellow Heights Apartments, Campbell to Harrison, 25th to 26th.
6   1991   Kiva at Diastole, SW corner, 25th and Charlotte.
7   1992   Hospital Hill Center, 2310 Holmes.

Hospital Hill, June 1995. View: W to E.

146

CHAPTER TEN

HAVE YOU SEEN HOSPITAL HILL LATELY?

I n the book *City of the Future: The Story of Kansas City*, Henry Haskell and Richard Fowler described the frenetic building boom in Kansas City in the first decade of the 20th century. The city had begun to construct General Hospital in 1905, and Henry M. Beardsley, mayor in 1906, liked to illustrate the times with a story about the city's growth.

Two traveling salesmen met in the smoking car of a train. The first salesman asked: "Have you seen Kansas City lately?" The second answered: "Yes, I was there two weeks ago." The first salesman replied: "But you should see it today."

On June 1, 1984, Homer C. Wadsworth returned to Kansas City to deliver the third Carl Migliazzo Lecture on graduation day at the UMKC School of Medicine. He opened his address with the following:

"Hospital Hill and the many institutions it serves is still something of a puzzle to the rest of the country. Many find it hard to believe that a state university could be persuaded to bail out a private university hanging on the financial ropes and with a rather uncertain future. But it happened. The suggestion that a city government would contract with a not-for-profit corporation to manage a public hospital, giving to this agency the power to hire its own personnel, purchase supplies as needed and work towards affiliate arrangements with a university that at the time was 140 miles away, has attracted considerable skepticism. But it happened. Many felt that it was stretching things a bit to assume that a wide range of state services could be persuaded to locate on Hospital Hill and to take over the expense of operating psychiatric services already present. But it happened. There were doubters as well as vested interests who opposed the notion that a medical school of quite different style and objectives could be put together. But it happened. Many had doubts about the effort to persuade the State of Missouri to appropriate general funds to offset in part the city's expense in providing services to medically indigent people. But it happened."

Homer Wadsworth died April 13, 1994. If he were able to come back to see Hospital Hill today he would likely smile and say: "But it happened."

But what will happen on Hospital Hill in the future? Mayor Emanuel Cleaver, for one, believes that the future of Hospital Hill depends upon market forces and state assistance.

"Given adequate funding by the state of Missouri," Cleaver said, *"with the advent of health*

147

reform and with the city's Health Department relocating there ... we could have on Hospital Hill one of the best healthcare — including mental health — operations in this country. The challenge before us is to get the funding from the state. It's embarrassing that we are ranked, I think, 48th in paid taxes by the citizenry and, of course, we also are ranked 48th for services provided. The President (Bill Clinton) said to me...that he *believed that Kansas City was ahead of the nation in both healthcare and welfare reform. I agree with him. We do have quality healthcare for all Kansas Citians. What we don't have are the dollars to assure Kansas Citians that all of the latest technology and equipment is going to be available. But, I think with what we have we are probably providing as good a healthcare service to this community as any city in the nation."*

VISIONS FOR THE FUTURE

Researchers in the past two years interviewed more than 50 people associated with Hospital Hill institutions to elicit information for this book, but also to leave an oral history of the times for future generations. The Western Missouri Historical Manuscript Collection, on the University of Missouri-Kansas City campus, will archive and make available these audio-taped and transcribed interviews sometime in the future. A list of interviewees appears in the bibliography section at the back of the book. Among those interviewed, several present-day leaders of Hospital Hill institutions agreed to share their thoughts about healthcare on Hospital Hill for this book, as follows.

Robijn K. Hornstra, M.D.,
chairman, Department of Psychiatry,
UMKC School of Medicine

"Psychiatric knowledge will be shared more and more with front-line practitioners in medicine, nursing and all kinds of professions. This will allow practitioners in such facilities as Health Maintenance Organizations to treat many psychiatric disorders in patients effectively; the psychiatrists will serve as consultants in the care of those persons.

For the care of the seriously mentally ill, the psychiatrist will play a pivotal role, not only in assisting mental health professionals through consultation, but also by helping patients achieve the best possible community adjustment.

A psychiatric department will not only have to train future psychiatrists, but be involved in the training of nurses, psychologists, activity therapists, social workers and all allied health professionals. Accredited training programs for mental health professionals are important, such as those in psychopharmacology and clinical psychology.

Our weekly General Staff Conference has been a hallmark of Western Missouri Mental Health Center for 40 years, and we will continue to gear up to train future healthcare practitioners who require psychiatric knowledge."

Gloria Joseph, M.S.W., superintendent,
Western Missouri Mental Health Center

"We still have the same goal we had many years ago, and that's to provide the best care we can. Comprehensive care is built into this Hill. Besides history, there's future here. We are trying to purchase land now, all the way down to Gillham. All we want to do is rearrange our facility so that we can access our front door from Gillham. With a new widened road on 22nd, we'll either go over it or under it. I can see in the future a maze of walkways, just like at Crown Center, that gets you over to Children's Mercy, Truman and the professional schools. Why not? The only thing we have to do is change our front door. Also in the future I foresee us managing informational systems and the data-gathering process much more proficiently than we have in the past. There's no reason why our public dollars can't make dollars for the public and enhance the quality of our care. The best thing I can say about Western Missouri is that it is a training-teaching hospital. We not only attract the psychiatrist, we are trying to take psychiatric nursing to even higher levels. Beyond all that, our vision is to become the number-one psychiatric facility in the nation."

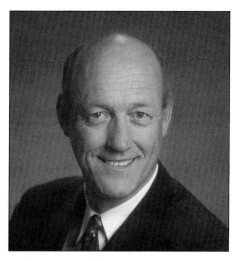

Dick Gregory, Ph.D., regional manager,
NW Region, Department of Mental
Health, State of Missouri

"New financial incentives will change mental healthcare in the future. Now we have two separate systems, a public, segregated system that really supports the private sector. When the private sector becomes overwhelmed, it often looks to us to take on that burden resulting in a separate and unequal system of care for the mentally ill. I foresee a delivery system on the Hill under healthcare reform that doesn't carve out and dump off certain kinds of disorders and disabilities and physical ailments that are psychiatric in nature, a system that will bring the mentally ill into the full light and let them be in the waiting room with the rest of us. Let them be knocking on the same doors that we knock on for our medicine and our care and de-mystify and de-stigmatize this population that deserves to be in the mainstream of daily life."

149

Marsha Kirk, M.P.A., executive director, Central Kansas City Mental Health Services

Randall L. O'Donnell, Ph.D., president, CEO, The Children's Mercy Hospital

Michael J. Reed, B.D.S., Ph.D., dean, UMKC School of Dentistry

"Now that the Department of Mental Health has established Western Missouri as a regional psychiatric hospital, we serve as the administrative agent of the Community Mental Health Center for Services. Because we are administratively separate, the hospital can focus on the emergency room and acute care and we can handle outpatient services. We still share a lot of support services like dietary, receiving and purchasing, and some other functions because we're in the initial stages of the separation, but we'll probably be separating those out soon. You really start looking at how you can better serve people in your community. We have a medication plan that serves 1,600 people. About half of those are enrolled in intensive case management. We have a rehab component where a team of folks works with people who have the skills to get involved in community activities. So we're trying to promote community integration, community involvement. For the people who aren't ready for that we also have a facility-based program where we teach people skills. We have so many programs, we have to be clear in setting priorities and determining what population we initially want to serve and do that very well."

"We have the juxtaposition with the medical school, yet we're independent from the medical school. We have the best of both worlds. The whole reason for existence, the raison d'etre, of a children's hospital is that children are not little adults.

Therefore, when it comes to the pecking order in determining allocations of resources, we can't allow children to be on the bottom of the list. Since children don't vote, children are on the bottom of the list on almost any other topic you can come up with in society. We can't allow children to be in anyone else's shadow. Children's Mercy Hospital needs to be independent. Here we sit in a nice position, though, because of the fact that we have the UMKC medical school, we have cooperative arrangements with TMC and longstanding relationships with KU Medical Center. The thing that is nice to me is that the Health Department is here. We have TMC, the dental school, Western Missouri; it is a nicely adjusted position of like-minded, committed entities."

"We need to work together. If healthcare reform comes along in a way that many anticipate, then there will be opportunities where physicians, dentists, nurses, nurse practitioners, pharmacists and other allied professions will all be working together. It may be a good idea to develop our facilities and our curriculums to tie into what kind of environment professionals will be working in when they graduate.

Everybody is going to benefit from having certain common-core courses and disciplines that all health professions participate in. But there will always be a sensitivity to look at the patient as more than just a mouth, more than just a foot, more than just an arm, an intestine, but try to look at patients and their health and prevention as a total ubiquitous professional concern. Under those circumstances, you structure future buildings in such a way that there is a common core of courses that could be given in a convenient fashion, in an efficient cost-effective way, where you mix students together — medicine, dentistry, pharmacy, etc. — in interactive situations so they would all become used to working with one another."

Nancy Mills, M.S.N., Ph.D., dean, University of Missouri-Kansas City School of Nursing

"The university is undergoing strategic planning now that includes a building on Hospital Hill that will house the Schools of Nursing and Pharmacy. I've seen the request for that building in the budget proposal for planning dollars, and I happily share a vision of all the health sciences together on the Hill. Nursing would like to add two additional programs, a generic four-year bachelor of science degree in nursing and one leading to a Ph.D.; we already offer a master's program and an R.N.-completion program. The community wants the generic program, and since no other public institution in Kansas City offers that, we must be sure that we implement the program at the right time with something unique."

James J. Mongan, M.D., executive director, Truman Medical Center Corporation, and dean, University of Missouri-Kansas City School of Medicine

"My overall perception about Hospital Hill institutions is that they are critically important in the future because of their major roles. Somebody has to train tomorrow's practitioners, and we're the ones doing that. I also feel strongly about the indigent-care role and the care for the uninsured, and we're also doing that on Hospital Hill. So these institutions represent an important societal resource and a bulwark for dealing with those important issues of education and indigent care. In addition to that kind of fundamental view, I would say that there is a lot to feel good about them. We are in the midst of a rebuilding era where we are firming up the infrastructure, if you will, to get us ready for the next 20 years. That's important. We have created close working relationships, and dampened whatever jealousies or competitions that might have existed in the past. We do see ourselves more as a team going forward now, and that is strong, good news for the next century."

Felix Sabates, M.D., clinical professor and chairman, Department of Ophthalmology, University of Missouri-Kansas City School of Medicine & president, Eye Foundation of Kansas City

"One of my favorite quotes displayed at our medical school says, 'If the patient doesn't feel better after he has seen you, you have failed as a physician.' You cannot cure all of the time, but you certainly can hope to enhance the patient's quality of life. Improved vision is vital in reaching this goal.

Many changes are occurring in the healthcare field, and the Eye Foundation will continue to provide quality eye care, which is accessible and cost-effective. It is important that we continue to educate highly trained, ethical physicians with a vision for excellence. Whatever happens in the healthcare arena, we need to be advocates for our patients, continue to be leaders in our field and be in the frontiers of advanced technology. And most importantly, we must make this medical care available to all persons regardless of their economic status. Seeing the future is our mission!"

Richard Biery, M.D., director, Health Department, Kansas City, Missouri

Jerry Stolov, M.B.A., executive director, Hospital Hill Health Services Corporation

Donald R. Smithburg, M.P.A., executive director, Truman Medical Center Charitable Foundation, and chief administrative officer, University of Missouri-Kansas City School of Medicine

152

"The most dramatic change in Kansas City has been the removal of communicable diseases until AIDS came along, and perhaps now, tuberculosis. One strain of multiple-drug resistant tuberculosis is virtually resistant to all our available medications, and there are even variations of that strain. We see tuberculosis that is partially resistant, and if we don't treat those patients correctly, absolutely correctly, we get into expensive care. In some cases we cannot treat patients for certain kinds of the disease; that probably came out of the AIDS epidemic. For people who won't take their medicines reliably, who forget, the shift is to directly observed therapy, where you watch the person take the medication or somebody watches them. We have not experienced much multiple-drug resistant tuberculosis in Kansas City, but one case recently wiped out our entire TB budget. Tuberculosis may well double this year in Kansas City, so we are keeping an eye on that."

"The doctors' corporation has created a successful working alliance between the University of Missouri-Kansas City Health Sciences schools and its primary teaching hospitals. The primary reason for the success of our institutions has been the excellent working relationship among HHHSC, medical school and TMC personnel. We have developed a partnership between physicians and administration and avoided the all-too-often adversarial relationship between medical faculty and administration. Our organizational framework has established all parties as equal partners in the processes that provide patient care delivery systems and undergraduate and postgraduate medical education.

"Undoubtedly, this relationship becomes increasingly important in maintaining success in a demanding and changing healthcare environment."

"When we started the most recent Hospital Hill master-plan process, we put everybody's future plans up on the board. Most of these plans have become real and have increased the campus footprint by a third. Most of the growth isn't occurring because institutions wanted to carve out new market niches. When we started planning, we were bursting at the seams just trying to keep up with the patient population. That's somewhat of a sad commentary about our society because it means more poor people require healthcare. An important aspect of this growth is the sense of campus and campus life that's reflected in the new housing, the new facilities and the expanded services we're able to offer. The Hill as a whole works cooperatively in planning both facilities and programming. Each institution constantly looks for ways to collaborate in a variety of venues: facility development, land use and shared infrastructure. We hope the campus develops a sense of neighborhood as well as a sense of home. That can only improve the urban core and the community at large."

E. Grey Dimond, M.D., distinguished professor of medicine, University of Missouri, and provost emeritus, UMKC

Eleanor B. Schwartz, D.B.A., chancellor, UMKC

"A lay board has run indigent-care hospitals in Jackson County for 33 years. The United States has been through riots, inner-city burnings, Medicare, Medicaid, Clinton's failed health bill, the demand for more doctors, the demand for rural doctors, everything that you can think about has been cataclysmic in America. In those 33 years there has never been a scandal associated with an indigent-care hospital in this town. There has never been a place where anyone has said: 'What did they do with the money?' Often times we've said: 'We don't have enough money,' but no one ever said we misspent it or that there was cheating about contractors. If I were taking my hat off to anyone it would be to Homer and Nate and the board that has changed, died out, come along, survived. And the doctors' corporation has always been worked over by somebody who wants to know what the doctors are doing with its money. But the doctors' corporation stands. The County Hospital has grown and thrived. TMC has made money — a charity hospital that's actually been able to turn money back at times. A med school that never was fully funded now has more applicants than almost any school in the United States for the openings that it offers. Not bad."

"When the University created its medical, nursing and dental schools, there was no question about locating them on Hospital Hill. The site represents UMKC's commitment to Kansas City and to the vitality of its city core as well as to our own health sciences mission.

Looking to the future, UMKC plans to expand that commitment. In the planning are new facilities for pharmacy and nursing. With the movement of the healthcare industry from a $40 billion industrial colossus to community and professional healthcare teams, strengthening our partnership with Hospital Hill is important to medicine and the community."

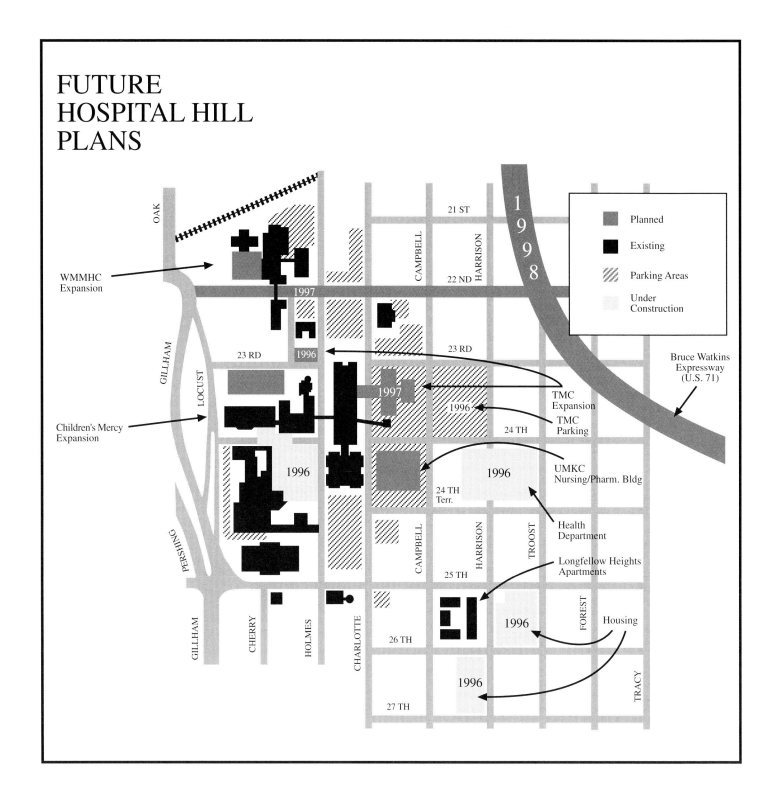

FUTURE
HOSPITAL HILL
PLANS

154

Planned

Existing

Parking Areas

Under
Construction

WMMHC
Expansion

Children's Mercy
Expansion

TMC
Expansion

TMC
Parking

UMKC
Nursing/Pharm. Bldg

Health
Department

Longfellow Heights
Apartments

Housing

Bruce Watkins
Expressway
(U.S. 71)

1998

1997

1996

1997

1996

1996

1996

1996

1996

OAK

GILLHAM

LOCUST

PERSHING

GILLHAM

CHERRY

HOLMES

CHARLOTTE

CAMPBELL

HARRISON

CAMPBELL

HARRISON

TROOST

FOREST

TRACY

21 ST

22 ND

23 RD

23 RD

24 TH

24 TH
Terr.

25 TH

26 TH

27 TH

APPENDIX A

THEN . . . AND NOW

These photographs depict exact sites of buildings or structures no longer standing, and the buildings or structures that now stand on the same spot.

2301 Holmes. The Bremer family's drugstore and apartments, SE corner of Holmes, 1924. Truman Medical Center at the same site today. Gracia Bremer, a 1918 graduate of the Kansas City College of Pharmacy, ran the drugstore for her father and inherited it after he died. Walter Cronkite once lived in the apartments. View: W to E.

23rd and Holmes, NE corner, 1929. The Kansas City College of Medicine and Surgery, a "diploma mill," closed in 1929 after a national scandal disclosed the school had issued thousands of medical degrees that only one state licensing board recognized. Truman Medical Center West parking lot today. View: SW to NE.

2220 Holmes. The backyard garden of the Research Hospital Nurses' Residence, ca. 1930s. Today, the spot serves the UMKC School of Nursing as a parking lot. View: SW to NE.

26th and Harrison, early 20th century. This was the city transit bus lot for many years. Today, Longfellow Heights Apartments offers nearby affordable housing for Hospital Hill students and workers. View: SE to NW.

157

25th and Holmes, NW corner. The Louis George Library opened in 1913, the gift of Mr. George, a longtime resident. The UMKC School of Dentistry occupies the ground today. View: SE to NW.

158

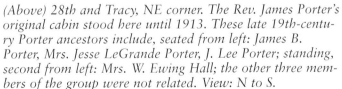

(Above) 28th and Tracy, NE corner. The Rev. James Porter's original cabin stood here until 1913. These late 19th-century Porter ancestors include, seated from left: James B. Porter, Mrs. Jesse LeGrande Porter, J. Lee Porter; standing, second from left: Mrs. W. Ewing Hall; the other three members of the group were not related. View: N to S.

(Above, right) The W. Ewing Porter and Ewing P. Hall residence at 2707 Tracy (demolished) faced east and stood just right of the group. View: W to E.

(Right) The B.W. Sheperd State School for Retarded Children stands today on the exact site of the cabin, facing north as the cabin did. View: NW to SE.

22nd and Charlotte, NE corner. The original (1883) Sumner School for black children sat in the West Bottoms on Wyoming between 9th and St. Louis. In 1903 the school, named for the Civil War abolitionist Charles Sumner, moved to a remodeled building at the SW corner of Washington and Madison Lane (N. 8th). In 1927, a new Sumner School opened at 2121 Charlotte, the former Karnes and S.F.B. Morse School. Sumner School burned in 1967. Today, the Kansas City Board of Education uses the grounds for facilities management purposes. The rock walls of the school's playground remain visible. View: N to S.

31st and Gillham. In 1878, the Little Sisters of the Poor transformed this former Orphans' Asylum into a home for the elderly. The building later was demolished. In 1926, the sisters moved to a new building at 53rd and Woodland. In 1952, the Jackson County Medical Society, now the Metropolitan Medical Society, built its office at the NW corner of the intersection. In the modern-day view, N to S, the home stood somewhat west and south of the former Hawn Bedding Co. sign. View: NE to SW.

23rd and McCoy (Kenwood), SE corner. Research Hospital completed this building in 1911. Today the Eye Foundation and the Hospital Hill Center occupy the site. View: NW to SE.

25th and Campbell, SE corner. A small stream that emptied into O.K. Creek at the 21st Street bluff caused this flood. An undocumented archival photograph, ca. 1910, notes on the back: "The vacant lot is 2511 Charlotte. House to south is Bleir's home. Then to left is a home occupied by former slave of Porter Family who had the right to live there all her life." Today the site contains a gravel parking lot. A U.S. Geological Survey map indicates the former creek bed ran through the current intersection of 25th and Charlotte, through the present-day medical school parking lot, then down to O.K. Creek. View: SE to NW.

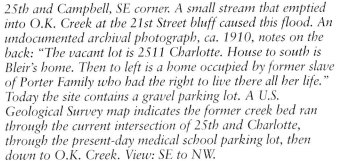
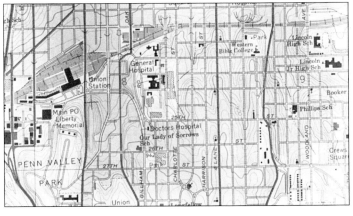

21st and Woodland. After Dr. Isaac Ridge earned a fortune as a builder, he purchased 40 acres on the east side of town and built his cross-shaped mansion, Castle Ridge, on the highest point. View: W to E. Today, Lincoln Academy stands on the site. View: SW to NE.

29th and Flora. Lakeside Hospital sat on Porter property overlooking Troost Lake, near the site of the 1832 Mormon school. The osteopathic hospital moved in the late 1960s to 8701 Troost Ave. Developers demolished the old hospital to build Lakeview Apartments. View: NW to SE.

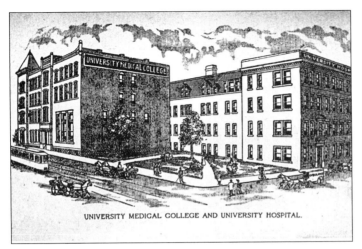

10th and Charlotte. University Medical College and University Hospital. Alums of old University Medical College would not recognize the site if they were alive today. Interstate 70 covers the ground now as this photo from the 10th Street overpass indicates. View: NW to SE.

162

This view of Main Street about 1910 demonstrates the continuity of Memorial, Signboard and Hospital Hills.

Same view today. View: N to S.

25th and Grand, looking west from Hospital Hill. (top left) 1906, the Westport Road. (top right) 1925, midtown improvements. (bottom left) 1971, excavation for Crown Center. (bottom right) The view today.

APPENDIX B

THE GEOLOGY OF HOSPITAL HILL

Richard J. Gentile
Professor of Geosciences
University of Missouri-Kansas City

Sedimentary rocks that underlie Hospital Hill formed during two widely separated intervals of geologic time, the Pennsylvanian Period and the Quaternary Period. The oldest rocks, Pennsylvanian, were deposited in vast shallow seas and on deltaic plains that covered the interior of the North American continent about 300 million years ago. The Quaternary rocks rest on the Pennsylvanian rocks and consist mainly of sediments deposited by wind and from melting continental ice sheets after the first glacial advance about one million years ago. Rock formations for the interval of time between these periods have eroded away; consequently almost 300 million years of Kansas City's earth history is unaccounted for and lost forever.

Hospital Hill, Signboard Hill and Memorial Hill all have similar geology, formed of Pennsylvanian rocks overlain by Quaternary rocks. Pennsylvanian rocks, commonly called bedrock, comprise a sequence of alternating layers, predominately limestone and shale. Limestone is composed of the mineral calcite and accumulated on the sea floor in the form of skeletal debris from invertebrate organisms and as minute crystals.

An extensive river system with headwaters in the present-day northern Appalachians, southern Canada, Arkansas and eastern Oklahoma transported sediments into the continental interior. These sediments were deposited along the shoreline forming deltaic lobes of soft mud tens of feet thick and hundreds of square miles in areal extent. The shoreline shifted position with each advance and retreat of the sea. At times the shoreline passed through the present-day greater Kansas City area, extending from Iowa across northwestern Missouri, southeastern Kansas and into Oklahoma. The deltaic system extended itself westward, following the retreating sea across the continental interior.

Through geologic processes the loose accumulation of sediments have been transformed into solid rock: layers of skeletal debris from invertebrate organisms and minute crystals of calcite have been altered to beds of limestone and the deltaic lobes of mud became shale. The record of fluctuating sea level can be read from the rock section. Each limestone-shale couplet represents one advance and one retreat of the sea across the interior of the continent. Geologists estimate that one complete cycle took 200,000 to 400,000 years.

Bedrock was deposited under essentially uniform conditions over large areas, consequently, the strata have similar physical properties and are continuous, except where they have been removed by erosion or excavated by humans. The excavation some 80 years ago on Main Street between what is now Pershing Road and 27th Street divided a northwest facing bluff into two hills, Signboard Hill and Memorial Hill, and exposed more than 50 feet of the rock section that underlies the city. For many years geologists visited this Main Street section to gain a better understanding of the geology of the region.

More than a million years ago, at a time before the climate grew colder and the first ice sheet advanced, stream drainage around Kansas City differed dramatically from the present pattern. The ancestral Missouri River entered northwestern Missouri near the present-day town of Tarkio and flowed in a southeastern direction to near Carrollton where the ancestral Kansas River joined it. As successive ice sheets advanced, the drainage of the Missouri shifted and flowed along the margin of the ice sheet. Of the several glacial advances, the Kansan, about 600,000 years ago, largely reshaped the land surrounding Kansas City. Glacial meltwater flowing along the edge of the Kansan ice sheet set the course of the present-day Missouri River. Ice lobes dammed the Missouri and Kansas Rivers at several places, forming large ice margin lakes that periodically overflowed.

One ice lobe several hundred feet thick crept into modern-day downtown Kansas City. The ice transported large quantities of sediment called glacial till, which includes numerous types of rocks and minerals. Many of the particles of ice-rafted till in the area came from as far north as southwestern Minnesota, the Great Lakes region and the Dakotas.

Although no evidence exists that continental glaciers reached as far south as Hospital Hill, an ice-age climate is evident from the thick blanket of loess that covers Pennsylvanian bedrock. Loess, a tan to yellowish-brown windblown silt, consists predominately of quartz and various other mineral and rock fragments. Individual particles are smaller than fine grains of sand but coarser than coarse clay. Recession of the ice sheet released large volumes of meltwater with a high sediment load, including an abundance of silt that inundated the flood plains of the Missouri and Kansas Rivers.

At the close of glaciation the flow of meltwater decreased, but a layer of sediment several feet thick remained on the flood plains. Westerly winds picked up the silt and deposited it on the river bluffs, following the contour of the land and draping itself over the hills and valleys. Some layers along Kansas City's bluffs exceed 75 feet, but diminish in thickness away from the major rivers, measuring 20 to 50 feet thick on Hospital and Signboard hills. Loess is semiconsolidated and easy to excavate. A common practice to level ground for building construction in pioneer Kansas City entailed pushing a hill into a valley.

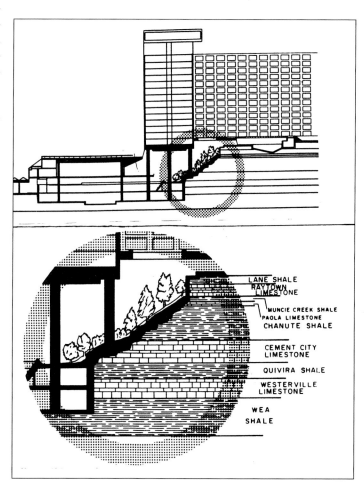

(top) Cross section of the Crown Center Hotel displays the waterfall and garden that architects designed to take advantage of the rocky north bluff of Signboard Hill.

(bottom) Cutaway view demonstrates the various rock units of the bluff (after Vineyard, 1974).

165

APPENDIX C
SELECTED BIBLIOGRAPHY

BOOKS & MONOGRAPHS

(Anonymous) *A Memorial Record of Kansas City and Jackson County, Missouri. Illustrated.* Chicago: The Lewis Publishing Company, 1896.

Brown, A. Theodore. *Frontier Community: Kansas City to 1870.* Columbia: University of Missouri Press, 1963.

_____. *The Politics of Reform: Kansas City's Municipal Government, 1925-1950.* Kansas City, Missouri: Community Studies, Inc., 1958.

_____, and Lyle W. Dorsett. *K.C.: A History of Kansas City, Missouri.* Boulder, Colorado: Pruett Publishing Co., 1978.

Bruce, Bessie Lee. *Reaching For A Dream.* Kansas City: Lawrence Collins Darden, Sr., 1979.

Case, Theodore S. *History of Kansas City, Missouri.* Syracuse: D. Mason, 1888.

Christ, Edwin A. *Missouri's Nurses: The Development of the Profession, Its Associations, And Its Institutions.* Columbia, Missouri: E. W. Stephens Publishing Company, 1957.

Cornuelle, Herbert C. *Mr. Anonymous.* Chicago: Henry Regnery Company, 1951.

Deatherage, Charles P. *Early History of Greater Kansas City Missouri and Kansas.* Kansas City, Missouri: Interstate Publishing Co., 1927.

Decker, Mary Bell and Clarence R. *A Place of Light: The Story of a University Presidency.* New York: Hermitage House, 1954.

Dickey, Kenneth McM. *A Man With Clay Feet.* Kansas City, Missouri: Mount Forest Press, 1953.

Dimond, E. Grey, M.D. *Take Wing! Interesting Things That Happened On My Way To School.* Kansas City, Missouri: Office of Educational Resources, University of Missouri-Kansas City School of Medicine, 1991.

Dorsett, Lyle W. *The Pendergast Machine.* Lincoln, Nebraska and London: University of Nebraska Press, 1968.

Dowling, Harry F. *City Hospitals: The Undercare of the Underprivileged.* Cambridge, Mass. and London, England: Harvard University Press, 1982.

Ehrlich, George. *Kansas City, Missouri: An Architectural History, 1826-1990.* Kansas City, Missouri: Historic Kansas City Foundation, 1990.

Ellis, Roy. *A Civic History of Kansas City, Missouri.* Springfield, Missouri: Press of Elkins-Swyers Co., 1930.

Epps, Robert L., S.T.M., Robert H. Barnes, M.D. and Thomas S. McPartland, Ph.D. *A Community of Concerns.* Springfield, Illinois: Charles C. Thomas, 1965.

Garwood, Darrell. *Crossroads of America, The Story of Kansas City.* New York: W.W. Norton & Co., Inc., 1948.

Glabb, Charles N. *Kansas City and the Railroads: Community Policy in the Growth of a Regional Metropolis.* Madison: State Historical Society of Wisconsin, 1962.

Goldstein, M. A. (Ed.) *One Hundred Years of Medicine and Surgery in Missouri.* St. Louis: St. Louis Star, 1900.

Goodwin, E. J., M.D. *A History of Medicine In Missouri.* St. Louis: W. L. Smith, 1905.

Gorman, Barbara M., Richard D. McKinzie and Theodore A. Wilson. *From Shamans To Specialists: A History of Medicine and Health Care in Jackson County Missouri.* Kansas City, Missouri: Jackson County Medical Society, 1981.

Green, George Fuller. *A Condensed History of the Kansas City Area: Its Mayors and Some V.I.P.s.* Kansas City, Missouri: The Lowell Press, 1968.

Haskell, Henry C. and Richard G. Fowler. *Kansas City: City of the Future: 1850-1950.* Kansas City, Missouri: Frank Glenn, 1950.

History of Jackson County, Missouri. Kansas City, Missouri: Union Historical Company: Birdsall & Williams, 1881. (Also Reprint. Cape Girardeau, Missouri: Ramfre Press, 1966.)

Jacobs, Joseph, D.D.S. *History of The University of Kansas City School of Dentistry: Kansas City-Western Dental College.* Kansas City, Missouri: Brown-White-Lowell Press, 1949.

Lanterman, Alice and Virginia Sheaff. *Your City and You: The Story of Kansas City: Volume IV.* Kansas City, Missouri: Board of Eduction, 1947.

Larsen, Lawrence H. and Nancy J. Hulston. *The University of Kansas Medical Center: A Pictorial History.* Lawrence: University Press of Kansas, 1992.

Lynaugh, Joan E. *The Community Hospitals of Kansas City, Missouri, 1870-1915.* New York & London: Garland Publishing, Inc., 1989.

Miller, W. H. *The History of Kansas City.* Kansas City, Missouri: Birdsall & Miller, 1881.

Olson, James. *Serving the University of Missouri.* Columbia: University of Missouri Press, 1993.

_____, and Vera Olson. *The University of Missouri: An Illustrated History.* Columbia: University of Missouri Press, 1988.

Pace, Patricia Ewing. *Kansas City: The Spirit, the People, the Promise.* Northridge, California: Windsor Publications, Inc., 1987.

Reddig, William M. *Tom's Town: Kansas City and the Pendergast Legend.* Philadelphia; New York: Lippincott, 1947; Columbia: University of Missouri Press, 1986.

Rhodes, Richard. *The Inland Ground.* New York: Atheneum, 1970.

Schirmer, Sherry Lamb and Richard D. McKinzie. *At the River's Bend: An Illustrated History of Kansas City, Independence and Jackson County.* Jackson County Historical Society. Woodland Hills, California: Windsor Publications, Inc., 1982.

Scofield, Carlton F. *A History of the University of Kansas City: Prologue to a Public Urban University.* Kansas City, Missouri: The Lowell Press, 1976.

Snider, W. Ray, M.D. and Robert Major Mathews, M.D. *Those Indomitable Surgeons Of Hospital Hill: A History of Surgeons at the Kansas City General Hospitals and Truman Medical Center.* Kansas City, Missouri: Office of Educational Resources, University of Missouri-Kansas City School of Medicine, 1989.

Spalding, C. C. *Annals of the City of Kansas.* Kansas City, Missouri: Van Horn & Abeel's Printing House, 1858. Reprint edition: Kansas City, Missouri: Frank Glenn Publishing Company, 1950.

Strickland, William A., Jr. *The Apothecary Trail in Greater Kansas City: The First 100 Years of Pharmaceutical Education.* Kansas City, Missouri: University of Missouri-Kansas City School of Pharmacy, 1985.

Swanson, Roger. *A History of the Children's Mercy Hospital, 1897-1961.* Kansas City, Missouri: Lowell Press, 1961.

Thompson, H. B. *"As We See 'Em."* Kansas City, Missouri: Lechtman Printing Co., 1905.

Where These Rocky Bluffs Meet: Including the Story of the Kansas City Ten-Year Plan. Kansas City, Missouri: Kansas City Chamber of Commerce, 1938.

Whitney, Carrie Westlake. *Kansas City, Missouri: Its History and Its People, 1808-1908.* Vols. I, II, III. Chicago: The S. J. Clarke Publishing Co., 1908.

REPORTS, DIRECTORIES, AND PUBLIC RECORDS

American Medical Directory. Volume I. Chicago: American Medical Association Press, 1906.
_____. Second Edition. Chicago: American Medical Association, 1909.
_____. Third Edition. Chicago: American Medical Association, 1912.
_____. Fourth Edition. Chicago: American Medical Association, 1914.
_____. Fifth Edition. Chicago: American Medical Association, 1916.
_____. Sixth Edition. Chicago: American Medical Association, 1918.
_____. Seventh Edition. Chicago: American Medical Association, 1921.
_____. Eighth Edition. Chicago: American Medical Association, 1923.
_____. Ninth Edition. Chicago: American Medical Association, 1925.
_____. Tenth Edition. Chicago: American Medical Association, 1927.
_____. Eleventh Edition. Chicago: American Medical Association, 1929.

Annual Report. A Year of Accomplishment. Kansas City, Missouri, 1950-51.

Annual Report of the Hospital and Health Board of Kansas City, Missouri.
_____. First Annual Report For Fiscal Year April 20, 1908 to April 19, 1909, inclusive.
_____. Second Annual Report For Fiscal Year April 20, 1909 to April 19, 1910, inclusive.
_____. Third Annual Report For Fiscal Year April 18, 1910 to April 17, 1911 Incl.
_____. Supplement to Report of Hospital and Health Board for 1914-1915.
_____. For the Year Ending April 21st, 1919.

A Report of Your City's Health Protection and Medical Care: 1951-1956. Health Department of Kansas City.

City Directory of Kansas City, Missouri. 1870, 1871, 1872. Kansas City, Missouri: Corbett, Hoye & Co.

City Directory of Kansas City, Missouri. Titles and publishers vary, 1881-1973.

Civic Improvement Committee (the committee of 1000). *A 10-Year Plan for Public Improvement in Kansas City.* Kansas City, Missouri: #33, Allied Printing Trades Council, 1931.

Community Studies, Inc. *A Study of the Public Health and Medical Care Needs of Jackson County and Kansas City, Missouri.* Kansas City, Missouri, July 1956.

Kansas City Area Hospital Association. *Community Report-Number 1, May, 1960.* Kansas City, Missouri, 1960.

Kansas City Health and Hospital Survey. Chamber of Commerce of Kansas City, Missouri. Kansas City, Missouri: Lechtman Printing Co., 1931.

Kansas City, Missouri Ordinances. 1859-1905. (Health related.)

Olson, Stanley W., M.D. *Survey of Physician Manpower in Missouri.* Missouri Commission on Higher Education, May 1968.

Report of the Citizens Study Committee On Kansas City — Jackson County Health Services. Kansas City, Missouri: October 15, 1960.

Report of Your City's Health Protection and Medical Care Program. Health Department of Kansas City, Missouri, 1951-56.

Report on Housing Conditions in Kansas City, Missouri. Kansas City, Missouri: Board of Public Welfare, June 1912.

State of Missouri. *Settlement Agreement and Release. William Volker Fund.* June 16, 1978.

University of Missouri-Kansas City School of Dentistry Alumni Directory, 1981. Montgomery, Alabama: College & University Press, 1981.

Your City and Its Government: City Manager's Centennial Year Report. Pp. 47-51. Kansas City, Missouri, 1950.

MEDICAL JOURNALS AND BULLETINS

Greater Kansas City Medical Bulletin. 1959-1976.

Jackson County Medical Journal. 1938-1958.

The Kansas City Medical Journal. 1871-1875.

The Kansas City Medical Record. 1884-1908.

The Kansas City Medical Index. 1896-1899.

The Kansas City Medical Index-Lancet. 1899-1910.

p.r.n. Newsletter of the University of Missouri-Kansas City School of Medicine, 21 vols., 1974-1994.

The Scalpel. University Medical College. Two volumes, 1909-1910.

Weekly Bulletin. Jackson County Medical Society, 1909-1932.

JOURNAL ARTICLES

Altomare, Edward P. "The Tuberculosis Hospital." *Weekly Bulletin.* Jackson County Medical Society. Commemorative Issue, Vol. L, No. 53, June 30, 1956, 1538-1540.

Bradford, Clyde Reed, M.D. "History of Kansas City General Hospital: Colored Division." *Jackson County Medical Journal.* Vol. XXVI, No. 41, October 8, 1932, 6-17.

Brunk, Josephine. "Brief History of the Kansas City Tuberculosis Hospital." *Jackson County Medical Journal.* XXVI, No. 39, September 24, 1932, 7-11.

Burns, B. I. "The Municipal Hospitals of Kansas City." *Weekly Bulletin.* Jackson County Medical Society, Commemorative Issue, Vol. L, No. 53, June 30, 1956, 1532-1536.

Ferris, Franklin. "State of Missouri v. B. Clark Hyde; Opinion of the Court." *Southwestern Reporter.* Vol. 136, 1911, 316-335.

"History of Kansas City General Hospital." *Jackson County Medical Journal.* Vol. XXVI, No. 40, October 1, 1932, 11-25.

McShane, Kevin C. "The 1918 Kansas City Influenza Epidemic." *Missouri Historical Review.* LXXXI, October 1968, 55-70.

Rodgers, Samuel U, M.D. "Kansas City General Hospital #2: A Historical Summary." *Journal of the National Medical Association.* September 1962, 525-543.

Welch, B.M. "The Radiological Department (Tuberculosis Hospital)." *Jackson County Medical Journal.* XXVI, No. 39, September 24, 1932, 11-13.

UNPUBLISHED MATERIAL

(Anonymous) *The Beginning at Little Blue.* Typed manuscript, Truman Medical Center East Archives, undated (ca. 1976).

(Anonymous) *Jackson County Hospital.* Typed manuscript, Truman Medical Center East Archives, undated.

(Anonymous) *TMC-East History: 1852-1982.* Typed manuscript, Truman Medical Center East Archives, undated.

Baer, Alvin J., M.D. *A History of the Kansas City General Hospitals.* Typed manuscript, Eye Foundation of Kansas City Archives, undated.

Bates, Sidney L. *Medicine Without Method: Kansas City, Missouri's General and Allied Hospitals Under The Department of Health, 1870-1962.* Master's thesis, University of Missouri-Kansas City, 1972.

Chronological Table. Principal Events and Activities: September, 1968 Through September, 1978. Office of Educational Resources, University of Missouri-Kansas City School of Medicine Archives, 1978.

Curran, Charles Edward. *Considerations of Hierarchy and Specialization With Special Reference to the Operation of a Municipal Hospital.* Ph.D. dissertation, Harvard University, 1960.

Ehrlich, George. *Historic Walking Tour of the Volker Campus of the University of Missouri-Kansas City.* UMKC Alumni Association, revised, 1984.

Edwards, Ralph Warren. *A History of Dental Education In Kansas City, Missouri.* Master's thesis, University of Kansas City, 1946.

Hornstra, Robijn K., M.D., *Psychiatry on Hospital Hill.* Typed manuscript, University of Missouri-Kansas City School of Medicine, Department of Psychiatry, 1994.

Johnson, Eleanor Moliere. *The Gathering of the Mormons in Jackson County.* Chapter III: "Securing the Land for Zion." Master's thesis, University of Nebraska, 1927.

Kilmer, Harry Edmund. *The Development of the Administration of Public Health and Safety. Kansas City, Missouri.* Master's thesis, University of Missouri, 1907.

Porter, Pierre R. *Reminiscences of Dr. David Rittenhouse Porter.* Typed manuscript, pp. 11-28, Western Historical Manuscript Collection, University of Missouri-Kansas City, undated.

Schauffler, Robert McEwen, M.D. *Biography of Edward William Schauffler, M.D.* Typed manuscript. Children's Mercy Hospital Archives, 1947.

Smithburg, Donald R. *Hospital Hill Planning In The '90s: A Unique Cooperative Adventure.* Typed manuscript. Truman Medical Center Charitable Foundation Archives, 1994.

Somogyi, Mary M., Anna Carlson and Mrs. S. Blake Gann Fursha. *A Brief History of the Kansas City General Hospital School of Nursing.* Typed manuscript. Western Historical Manuscript Collection, ca. 1960.

Sutton, Mary Cecile. *A History of the Kansas City, Missouri General Hospital.* Master's thesis, University of Chicago, 1946.

Twyman, Leo W., M.D. and Lyddall. *A Report of the Principal Contagious Diseases Occurring In and About Independence, Mo. During the Period from 1844 to 1880.* Typed manuscript, Western Historical Manuscript Collection, undated.

Wagner, Patricia Youmans. *Voluntary Associations in Kansas City, Missouri: 1870-1900.* Ph.D. dissertation, University of Kansas City, 1962.

Wenner, Herbert A. and Sydney F. Pakula. *The History of the Children's Mercy Hospital.* Typed manuscript, Children's Mercy Hospital Archives, 1984.

Winters, Shirley, R.N., and Charlotte Cooper Williams, R.N. *History of the Kansas City General Hospital & Medical Center School of Nursing.* Typed manuscript, Western Historical Manuscript Collection, ca. 1968.

AUDIOTAPED INTERVIEWS

Luisita Archer, Ph.D.	June 8, 1994	Nancy Mills, Ph.D.	July 6, 1994
John Barnard, M.D.	June 13, 1994	James J. Mongan, M.D.	June 2, 1995
Sid Bates	November 4, 1993	Stuart Munro, M.D.	April 15, 1994
Carol Belt, R.N.	February 10, 1994	Edward Nelson, D.D.S.	June 16, 1994
Richard Berkley	July 1, 1994	Richardson K. Noback, M.D.	January 15, 1994/May 27, 1994
Richard Biery, M.D.	November 23, 1993	Randall O'Donnell, Ph.D.	February 8, 1994
Kathleen Bond, Ph.D.	May 1994	John O'Hearne, M.D.	July 14, 1994
Donald Chisholm	February 11, 1994	Lloyd Olson, M.D.	June 16, 1994
Mayor Emanuel Cleaver, II	June 23, 1994	Carl Peterson, M.D.	June 27, 1994
Charles Curran, Ph.D.	June 28, 1994	Michael Reed, B.D.S., Ph.D.	July 5, 1994
Ilus Davis	December 16, 1993	Nancy Richart	April 26, 1994
E. Grey Dimond, M.D.	April 28, 1995	Samuel U. Rodgers, M.D.	November 9, 1993
Richard Dreher, M.D.	June 6, 1994	Felix N. Sabates, M.D.	March 9, 1994
Adele Eberhart	May 3, 1994	Donald R. Smithburg, M.P.A.	June 9, 1995
Rachel Goldman	June 29, 1994	Jack Stewart, D.D.S.	May 20, 1994
Dick Gregory, Ph.D.	April 28, 1994	Jerry Stolov	May 24, 1994
Gerald Hoff, M.D.	November 29, 1993	Russell Sumnicht, D.D.S.	June 7, 1994
Robijn K. Hornstra, M.D.	April 19/26, 1994	Herman Sutherland	June 15, 1994
Harry S. Jonas, M.D.	May 27, 1994	Charles Wheeler, M.D., J.D.	November 9, 1993/July 5, 1994
Carolyn Jones, R.N.	June 28, 1994	Herbert Wenner, M.D.	May 20, 1994
Gloria Joseph, M.S.W.	April 26, 1994	Western Missouri Mental	April 21, 1994
Marsha Kirk, M.P.A.	May 4, 1994	Health Center Round Table	
James Limestall, D.D.S.	June 27, 1994	(Betty Ergovich, Ruth Lewis,	
Albert P. Mauro	June 2, 1994	Cornelius Neufeld,	
Kendall McNabney, M.D.	May 24, 1994	and Dorothy Johnson)	
Rosa Miller, R.N.	June 23, 1994		

APPENDIX D

ACKNOWLEDGMENTS

Donald R. Smithburg conceived the idea of a history of Hospital Hill and obtained the needed financial support to publish it. Nancy Whitnell Harris and Laura Patterson conducted interviews with a number of people to obtain information about public healthcare in Kansas City, Missouri and Jackson County. David Boutros, associate director of UMKC's Western Historical Manuscript Collection offered suggestions on sources, and UMKC archives assistant Marilyn Burlingame time and again uncovered interesting photographs, illustrations and facts that appear in the book. Charles E. Curran offered numerous insights about public healthcare in Kansas City, dating to the early 1950s. Carol Belt, volunteer archivist for The Children's Mercy Hospital, a longtime nurse there but retired now, supplied photographs and details about Mercy and Wheatley-Provident. Sid Bates of the Kansas City, Missouri Health Department provided access to city reports and ordinances; his master's thesis on Kansas City's Health Department offered several investigative avenues. Dory DeAngelo performed vital research on early Kansas City history and events, and Sara Nyman and members of the staff of Missouri Valley Special Collections, Kansas City, Missouri Public Library graciously located photographs and illustrations for reproduction. Richard Gentile, UMKC Geosciences professor, helped establish the geology and topographic relationship of present-day Hospital Hill, Signboard Hill and Memorial Hill.

Many of the above read the manuscript and offered valuable suggestions.

UMKC's Health Sciences Library staff members Jeanne Sarkis and Ana Fernandez answered repeated research queries and book-loan requests. UMKC School of Medicine staff members Jeri Parish and Ann Aylward assisted with manuscript preparation; Kerry Kirk, audiovisual supervisor, coordinated interview transcriptions; Barbara Rauscher, photography supervisor, and Matt Miquelon and John Carmody processed hundreds of images, some their own; Zig Zobans designed the computer-imaged maps in the book.

Several editors pointed out obscure and meaningless sentences to recast, lined out unneeded modifiers, questioned dubious claims with margin challenges and generally created orderliness in the narrative text. Their work has saved the author much embarrassment at publication time. Carina Gronlund helped proofread and correct the manuscript. Any inaccuracies that remain are the author's responsibility.

The author thanks the Truman Medical Center Charitable Foundation, the University of Missouri-Kansas City and other sponsoring Hospital Hill organizations for the opportunity to bring these photographs and information to the attention of interested readers.

Photographic and Illustration Credits

Our thanks to the many organizations and individuals who allowed us to reproduce or use photographs and illustrations to help readers enjoy a visual history of public healthcare in Kansas City, Missouri. Numerals indicate page numbers; top (t), bottom (b), middle (m), left (l) and right (r) designate page positions. In some cases, only one page number appears if all photographs or illustrations on that page come from the same source.

ORGANIZATIONS

CCDR Rodriguez, Inc.
Page 135(t).

Children's Mercy Hospital
Pages 25, 34(t), 34(bl), 38, 39, 62(t), 66(b), 67(t), 70(tm), 74, 75, 76, 77, 130(b), 136(br), 150(tm).

Eye Foundation of Kansas City
Pages 128(b), 140, 141, 151(tr).

Harry S. Truman Library
Page 113(b).

Jackson County Historical Society Archives
Pages 8(bl), 31(b).

John F. Kennedy Library
Page 64.

Kansas City Area Transit Authority
Page 157(tr).

Kansas City, Missouri Health Department
Page 152(tl).

Kansas City, Missouri Public School District
Page 159(tl).

Kansas City Museum
Pages 65(b), 71.

Missouri Department of Natural Resources
Jerry D. Vineyard
Pages 163(bl), 164(t), 165(b).

Missouri Valley Special Collections
Kansas City Public Library
Kansas City, Missouri
Pages VI(b), 2(tr), 2(b), 3(b), 8(t), 8(br), 9(l), 15(br), 17(t), 18, 20(tr), 20(br), 28(b), 30(b), 33(tr), 44, 45(bl), 50(bl), 51(tl), 51(tr), 61(b), 62(b), 68, 83(tl), 83(b), 84(b), 85(b), 86(b), 87(b), 96(tr), 97, 101(b), 157(tl), 158(tl), 159(bl), 160(ml), 161(tl), 161(bl).

Research Medical Center
Pages 13(b), 29(tl), 29(b).

Saint Luke's Hospital Archives
Pages 24(b), 63(tl).

Shaffer Kline & Warren P.A.
Page 70(b).

Truman Medical Center Charitable Foundation
Page 130(t).

Truman Medical Center East (Jackson County Hospital)
Pages 5(t), 89, 115(b), 131.

Truman Medical Center West (Kansas City General Hospital & Medical Center)
Pages 12(tr), 32(tr), 35(b), 36(tr), 42(tl), 43(t), 66(t), 81, 82, 83(tr), 84(t), 85(t), 86(t), 96(tl), 98(b), 102(b), 103(b), 104, 105, 108, 110, 111(tl), 111(b), 113(t), 114, 115(t), 117(bl), 117(br), 118, 119(b), 121(br), 124(ml), 142(br), 156(bl).

University of Health Sciences-College of Osteopathic Medicine Alumni Association
Page 60(br).

United States Geological Survey
Page 160(br).

University of Kansas Medical Center Archives
Page 30(t).

University of Missouri-Kansas City
Archives
Pages 33(bl), 33(br), 35(l), 69(l), 72, 73, 87(t), 88(r), 92, 93, 101(t), 102(t), 116, 117(tl), 119(tl), 155(l).

University of Missouri-Kansas City
Health Sciences Library
Pages 4(b), 7, 14(b), 26, 27(t), 29(tr), 35(t), 37(b), 42(tr), 42(b), 45(t), 46(b), 47, 48, 54, 55, 56, 57, 63(bl), 63(br), 69(b), 80(t), 90(tr), 91(tr), 91, 99(bl), 100, 162(tl).

University of Missouri-Kansas City
School of Dentistry
Office of Biomedical Communications
Photography Department
Pages 13(t), 117(tr), 150(tr).

University of Missouri-Kansas City
School of Medicine
Office of Educational Resources
Photography Department
Pages VII, 119(tr), 120, 121(tl), 121(tr), 121(bl), 124(t), 128(t), 129, 132, 133, 134, 135(b), 136(tl), 136(tr), 137(tr), 138, 139, 142(tl), 143(t), 146, 149(tl), 151(tl), 151(tm), 152(tm), 155(r), 156(tr), 156(br), 157(b), 158(tr), 158(br), 159(tr), 159(br), 160(tr), 160(mr), 161(tr), 161(br), 162(tr), 162(br), 163(br).

University of Missouri-Kansas City
School of Pharmacy
Page 33(tl).

University of Missouri-Kansas City
University Communications
Page 153(tr).

Wall of Fame Collection
Bruce R. Watkins Cultural Heritage Center
Page 69(t).

Western Historical Manuscript Collection
Pages V, 2(tl), 3(t), 4(t), 5(b), 9(r), 10, 12(tl), 12(b), 14(t), 15(t), 15(bl), 16, 17(b), 19, 20(tm), 20(l), 21, 24(tl), 24(tr), 27(b), 28(t), 31(tl), 31(tr), 32(tl), 32(bl), 32(br), 36(tl), 36(b), 37(tl), 37(tr), 45(br), 46(t), 49(tl), 49(tr), 50(t), 51(b), 60(tl), 60(tr), 61(t), 63(tr), 67(b), 70(tl), 80(b), 87(b), 88(l), 90(tl), 96(b), 99(t), 119(tl), 142(bl), 156(tl), 158(lm), 158(rm), 160(tl), 162(bl), 163(tl), 163(tr).

Western Missouri Mental Health Center
Pages 98(t), 99(br), 112, 122, 124(b), 136(bl), 137(tl), 137(bl), 137(br), 149(tm), 149(tr), 150(tl).

INDIVIDUALS

Mike Bushnell Postcard Collection
Page 65(t).

Bill Chisholm Photographic Collection
Page 103(t).

E. Grey Dimond, M.D.
Page 153(tl).

Evelyn Gunn Fisher
Page 143(b).

Richard J. Gentile, Ph.D.
Pages VI(t).

Mary Ann Kuchta
Page 111(tr).

Roger W. Metz
Page 142(tr).

Donald R. Smithburg
Page 152(tr).

Arthur P. Taliaferro, M.D.,
James S. Johnson, M.D.
& Gloria Swain
Pages 34(br), 43(b), 52, 60(bl).

Zig Zobans
Pages VIII, 22, 40, 58, 78, 94, 106, 126, 144, 154.

173

Sponsoring Institutions

174

175

HOSPITAL HILL
AN ILLUSTRATED ACCOUNT
OF PUBLIC HEALTHCARE INSTITUTIONS
IN KANSAS CITY, MISSOURI

was digitally composed in Sabon, Copperplate Gothic and Madrone
and printed on 100# gloss coated enamel text.